Subantarctic New Zealand

A Rare Heritage

Framed by megaherbs: a light-mantled sooty albatross at its nest high above Fly Harbour, Adams Island. ANDRIS APSE

Principal photographers

- ANDRIS APSE andris@andrisapse.com
- TUI DE ROY photos@rovingtortoise.co.nz
- KIM WESTERSKOV kim.westerskov@xtra.co.nz

SUBANTARCTIC NEW ZEALAND

A Rare Heritage

NEVILLE PEAT

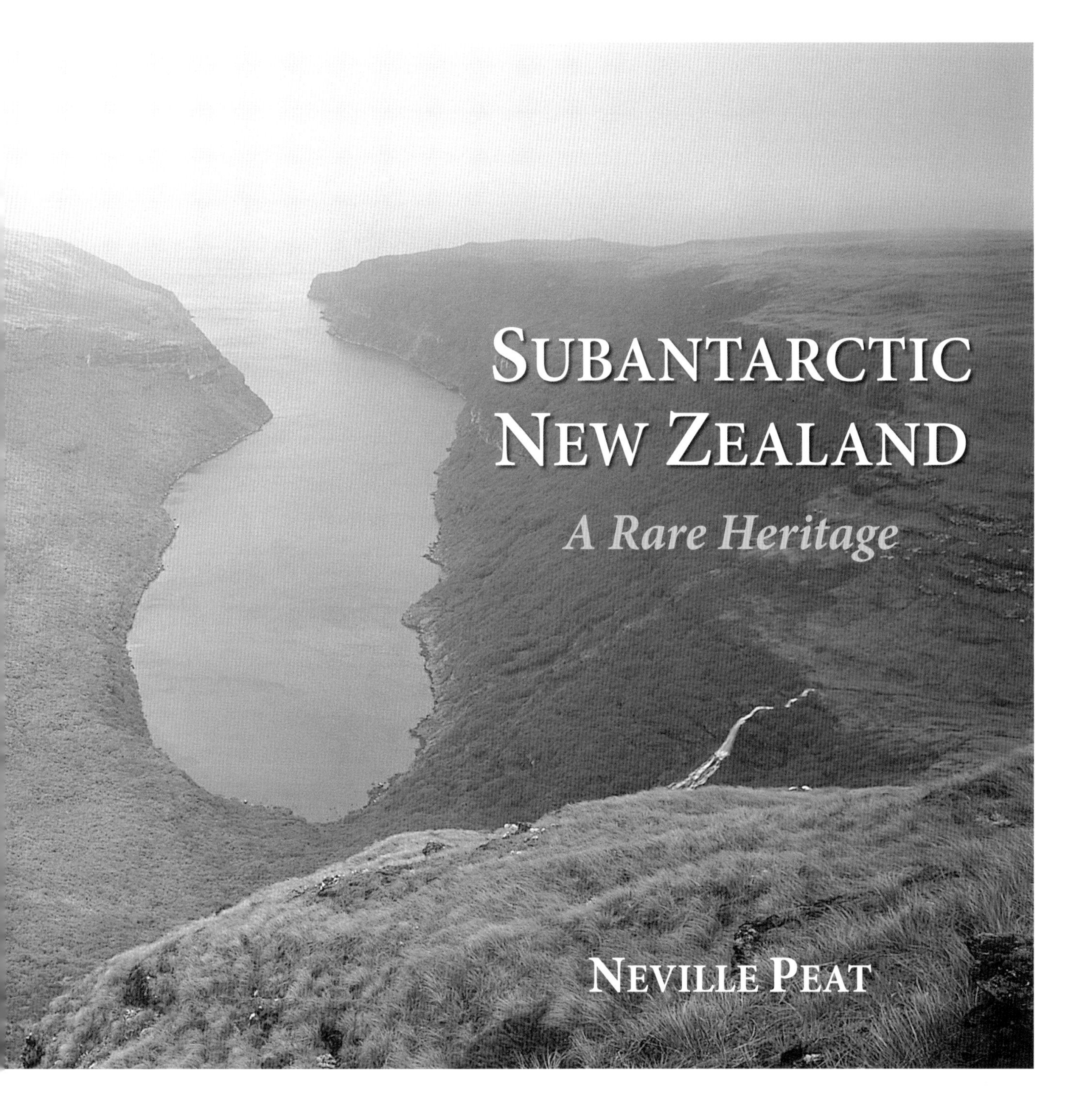

ACKNOWLEDGEMENTS

To Jeremy Carroll for project management and to Carol West and Rachael Egerton for the bulk of the editing advice, many thanks. Thanks also to Karl Blaas who coordinated the photographic side. Other Department of Conservation staff who contributed advice, information and practical assistance: Alan Baker, Sean Cooper, Mark Day, Paul Dingwall, Eric Edwards, Greg Lind, Janice Molloy, Chris Pugsley, Brian Rance, Chris Rance, Kath Walker, Ian West, Ian Wilkinson. Julie Campbell produced an outstanding collection of maps. NIWA's Paul Sagar and David Thompson supplied information on their southern Buller's albatross and eastern rockhopper penguin studies. James Newman, of the University of Otago, and Scott Shaffer et al assisted with information on the titi work at The Snares. Derek Onley commented on albatross nomenclature.

Special thanks to the following for the use of photographs: the principal photographers Andris Apse, Tui de Roy and Kim Westerskov, and also David Agnew, Brian Ahern, Alexander Turnbull Library, Chris Carroll, Wynston Cooper, Mike Dellamore: *R.V. Tiama*, Paul Dingwall, Barry Harcourt, Mike Meads, Rod Morris, Brian Patrick, Neville Peat, Rakiura Museum, Brian Rance, Chris Rance, Darren Scott, Tim Shaw, Southland Museum and Art Gallery, State Library of Victoria, Graeme Taylor, Pete Tyree, Kath Walker, Geoff Walls, Kennedy Warne, Chrissy Wickes. Thanks also to Jo Ogier for use of her artwork.

Thanks to the Alexander Turnbull Library, Wellington, New Zealand, for the following photographs:

Page 78: From Drawings & Prints Collection – Enderby; by Charles Henry Enderby 1798?–1876; Watercolour 176 x 260 mm; Port Ross, Auckland Islands, between 1850 and 1852?
Reference Number A-093-008

Page 82: From the Making New Zealand Collection; Auckland Islands; photographer unknown; Castaway huts on Disappointment Island, Auckland Islands.
Reference Number F-1317-1/2-MNZ

Page 83: Bollons Album; Auckland Islands, 1908; photographer unknown; K. Knudson (3rd Mate), M. Puhl, R. Ellis and J. Grattan on board the 'Hinemoa' alongside a wooden frame of what had been a canvas boat. The boat was used by survivors of the Dundonald shipwreck. Reference Number PA1-q-228-09-3

Page 84: From Photographic Archive, M.H. Redican Collection; photographer unknown; Wireless operator (C. Young) on the job, Campbell Island; 1939–1945. Reference Number PAI-f-169-05-50

Page 86: From Drawings & Prints Collection – Le Breton; by Louis Auguste Marie Le Breton; Hand-coloured lithograph 183 x 322 mm; Ilot basattique dans la baie Sarah's Bosom. Dessine par L. Le Breton; lithe par Meyer; lith. de Thierry freres, Paris - Paris; Gide Editeur [1846] Reference Number B-052-014

Photographs on pages 57, 65 and 88
Crown Copyright: Department of Conservation Te Papa Atawhai

MAPS

The Five Groups

Published by the Department of Conservation Te Papa Atawhai

ISBN 0-478-14088-6
First published 2003
Revised edition 2006

Produced by Department of Conservation
Southland Conservancy
P.O. Box 743, Invercargill.

Cover and book design by Jenny Cooper
Maps by Julie Campbell

Printed by Tablet Colour Print, Dunedin

Contents

‘There are days when these islands are enveloped in an unsurpassed bleakness and days of bright blue clarity when they are the most invigorating and wild places on earth.’

Excerpt from World Heritage Area nomination, 1997

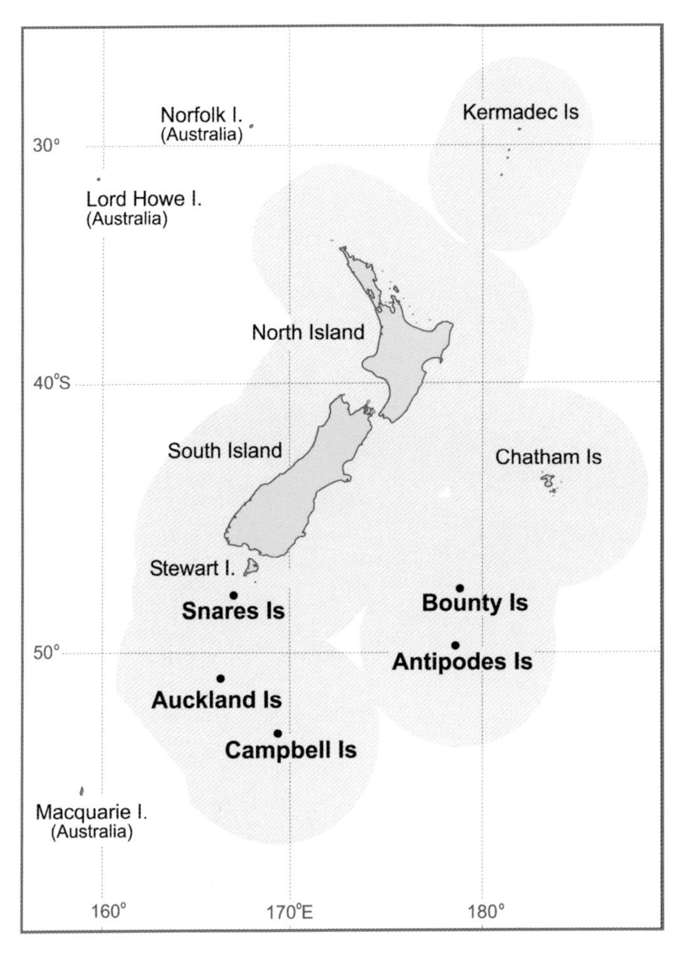

The New Zealand Exclusive Economic Zone

A World of Their Own

TO THE SOUTH of mainland New Zealand is a boundless sweep of ocean staked out by five groups of islands, remote from each other and from the New Zealand mainland, each group exhibiting a character of its own. These are the New Zealand subantarctic islands – The Snares, Bounty, Antipodes, Auckland and Campbell Islands. No two are the same, either physically or in terms of the life they support. What they do have in common, though, besides their far-flung nature, is a blue commons called the Southern Ocean, where currents and water masses freewheel, unimpeded by land.

Spanning six degrees of latitude, from 47 to 52 degrees south, the five island groups occupy the stormy latitudes of the Roaring Forties and Furious Fifties, known also

A rock overhang on the southwest side of Campbell Island, with Rocky Bay and its islets in the distance. ANDRIS APSE

as the Albatross Latitudes. The islands, uninhabited by humans, are rugged, lonely havens where life forms are not only remarkable but also sometimes outlandish and improbable. The biota contends with a challenging climate – cool, wet, windy and thoroughly oceanic. Resilience is taken for granted. Superlative natural values are only part of the story, however. Mix in an air of mystery nourished by the outpost nature of the islands and a history of sealing, whaling, shipwrecks, ill-fated enterprise and human frailty and you have a truly unique region.

The majestic flying style of albatrosses is well demonstrated by this Campbell mollymawk.
TUI DE ROY

These islands are among the world's wildest places. Some are close to pristine. The larger ones have suffered from the introduction of alien animals in the past but, island by island, animal by animal, they are slowly being cleared of introduced fauna and restored to something like their original condition. Most of the fauna – and elements of the flora as well – are dependent on the sea. Everywhere the horizon is blue and seemingly limitless. Together with Macquarie Island, an Australian territory to the southwest of Campbell Island, these are the only subantarctic islands in the Pacific sector of the Southern Ocean. The nearest Southern Ocean islands east of the New Zealand region are the very cold South Shetland Islands – 8,000 km distant.

Each of the New Zealand groups lays claim to a unique assemblage of fauna and flora. Seabirds and members of the seal family, the pinnipeds, dominate the fauna, and most of them are faithful to the islands where they breed. Once established, they do not usually stray to distant breeding grounds as 'island-hopping' is inhibited by the extent of ocean between the groups. Diversity and endemism – the latter describing life forms found nowhere else – are recurring themes in this region, and when played together, the two themes conjure up one superlative after another.

'Seabird capital' is one such claim. If, as is widely regarded, New Zealand hosts the most diverse collection of seabirds in the world, then the subantarctic islands are surely the principal flag bearers of the title. More than 40 seabird species – at least 11 percent of all the world's seabirds – breed in the New Zealand subantarctic region, and over 120 species have been observed at the islands or in the surrounding ocean. They range in size from tiny storm petrels that dance on the sea's surface to majestic albatrosses that circumnavigate the Southern Ocean with three-metre wingspans. Ten of the world's albatross species – some 40 percent – breed in the region, five of them nowhere else. The five comprise three great albatrosses (Gibsons, Antipodean and southern royal) and two albatrosses in the mollymawk group (Campbell and white-capped), although one white-capped nest has been found at the Chatham Islands.

A pair of Campbell mollymawks perform a courtship dance at their nest at the North Cape colony, Campbell Island.
TUI DE ROY

Auckland Island shags, endemic to this group of islands, resting and preening in the late-afternoon sun near North East Cape, Enderby Island. ANDRIS APSE

Among the world-wide family of petrels, shearwaters, fulmars and prions, 21 species or 30 percent breed on New Zealand subantarctic islands. Penguins, too, are special in the New Zealand subantarctic region. Of four penguin species breeding here, two (Snares crested and erect crested) are endemic to the region. The region's cormorants or shags highlight endemism at a local level. The Campbell Island shag, Auckland Island shag and Bounty Island shag are found only at their groups, with the Bounty Island shag claiming a world record as the rarest of all cormorants.

Continuing the marine theme, one of the rarest members of the seal family is based at the Auckland and Campbell Islands: the New Zealand or Hooker's sea lion. Its population in 2006 was estimated to be 12,000. With its main breeding range confined to just four sites in the Auckland Islands, the species is judged to be vulnerable to mass mortality events such as that which occurred in early 1998 (see page 48).

A sea lion negotiates an underwater kelp forest at the Auckland Islands. KIM WESTERSKOV

Southern elephant seals breed and haul out at Antipodes and Campbell Islands, and southern right whales, staging a recovery after decimation early last century, have chosen Port Ross in the Auckland Islands as their main breeding ground.

Rarity and abundance sometimes reside together at these islands. Millions of seabirds breed at The Snares, occupying just about every available nesting space on this relatively small set of islands, which are home as well to a few rare land birds and rare plants.

A World Heritage

NEW ZEALAND has applied the highest form of protection to its five subantarctic island groups in honour of the rare and special life they support. All five groups are national nature reserves – a designation that acknowledges their extraordinary natural and conservation status. Access is restricted and the Department of Conservation, the government agency responsible for the islands, actively protects the islands from harmful impacts.

In December 1998 the five groups were listed as a World Heritage Area. This United Nations listing recognises the 'outstanding universal value' and 'superlative natural phenomena' of the islands, which line up now with natural heritage areas such as the Great Barrier Reef and the Grand Canyon.

The five groups were assessed for World Heritage listing on the basis of four criteria, with strong weight given to their biodiversity, natural habitats and 'threatened species of outstanding universal value from the point of view of science or conservation'. The World Heritage nomination emphasised the role of the islands as 'havens of endemism'.

They form New Zealand's third World Heritage Area (after Tongariro National Park and Te Wāhipounamu-Southwest New Zealand).

A sea of purple daisies colours the western slopes of Campbell Island: *Pleurophyllum speciosum* at peak flowering time. TUI DE ROY

No group demonstrates the role of the New Zealand subantarctic islands as breeding grounds for marine species more graphically than the Bounty Islands. Over summer, the group's 20 small islands – proverbial specks in the ocean and bare of vegetation – are teeming with mollymawks, penguins, shags and fur seals.

Whereas marine species are dominant and conspicuous, they do not have the New Zealand subantarctic islands to themselves. Land birds and small invertebrate animals, including insects, are surprisingly numerous, diverse and in some cases breathtakingly rare. Freshwater fish life appears limited to a single galaxiid species (koaro *Galaxias brevipinnis*, at Auckland and Campbell Islands). No amphibians or reptiles, including lizards, have been found in the New Zealand subantarctic region.

The land birds indicate, through their diversity, just how long these islands have been isolated, both from mainland New Zealand and from each other. No fewer than 15 species are subantarctic endemics, with one species – the Campbell Island snipe – an astonishing discovery in recent times. A rare duck, the flightless Campbell Island teal, is making a comeback at the Campbell group. The Auckland Islands group also has its own snipe and teal together with an endemic rail, dotterel, tomtit and pipit. At the Antipodes, four endemic land birds include the Antipodes Island parakeet, which is often seen foraging in and around penguin colonies – an unusual association.

The plant life of the New Zealand subantarctic region is no less unusual. In recognition of the richness, special forms and unique associations, the World Conservation Union (IUCN) has designated the region a world centre of floristic diversity. Vascular plants number about 250, with 35 found only in the region and several found only at a single island or group. Except for the Bounty group, the islands are well vegetated. The Snares and two islands in the Auckland group, Adams and Disappointment, are among the world's most natural islands, being largely unaffected by human activity or alien animals. Campbell Island is set to join them, following removal of sheep and rats.

Forest reaches its southern limit in the South-west Pacific at these islands, with The Snares forest dominated by the large tree daisy *Olearia lyallii*, reaching a height of over five metres, and the Auckland Islands supporting southern rata *Metrosideros umbellata*, a flowering tree in

ISLANDS AT A GLANCE

Groups:	THE SNARES	BOUNTY Is	ANTIPODES Is	AUCKLAND Is	CAMPBELL Is
Area:	328 ha	135 ha	2,097 ha	62,560 ha	11,331 ha
Latitude:	48° 02′ S	47° 45′ S	49° 41′ S	50° 44′ S	52° 33′ S
Distance from Sth Is:	200 km	700 km	870 km	460 km	700 km
European discovery:	1791	1788	1800	1806	1810
Reserved:	1961	1961	1961	1934 (Adams I. 1910) Marine reserve 2003	1954

the myrtle family. No comparable forest exists at the Campbell or the Antipodes groups, where tussock grasslands and herbfields are more extensive than the tracts of shrubland.

Significantly larger than the other groups, the Auckland Islands has the richest plant life, ranging from forest to fellfield. The four vegetated groups support megaherb species – the region's most eye-catching plants.

Why is the flora and fauna of the New Zealand subantarctic region so diverse compared to many other Southern Ocean islands? A key reason is the region's mid-latitudinal location and a climate that is essentially cool-temperate. Only those islands close to the Antarctic Convergence, a major ocean boundary where various water masses meet, are regarded as truly subantarctic. Most of these islands are in the Atlantic Ocean sector, lying between latitudes 51 degrees and 63 degrees (except for Gough Island at 40 degrees). In this zone the mean annual temperatures are 1° to 5°C – too cold for trees. Islands with a climate comparable to that of the New Zealand groups include the Falkland Islands, Tristan da Cunha and Gough Island in the Atlantic Ocean sector and Amsterdam and Ile Saint-Paul in the South Indian Ocean.

In the New Zealand subantarctic region, the flora is transitional between mainland New Zealand's temperate pattern and the less diverse, more southerly subantarctic flora, which is lacking in woody species. Campbell Island, New Zealand's coldest island, lies north of the Antarctic Convergence by three or four degrees of latitude, and its woodiest plant life comprises thickets of the shrubby grass tree *Dracophyllum longifolium*.

Isolation is another contributor to diversity. The New Zealand islands, lying midway between two great oceanic

Getting There

Remote and surrounded by a wild ocean, the New Zealand subantarctic islands are not easily visited. Transport by sea is on a charter basis only, whether by tourist vessels or by vessels engaged to carry management or scientific personnel.

Royal New Zealand Navy frigates occasionally visit Campbell and Auckland Islands for training purposes and to convey conservation staff and scientists and their equipment.

Air access is restricted to helicopters as there are no airstrips for fixed-wing aircraft at the islands. The first helicopter flight to the subantarctic region from mainland New Zealand was by a Squirrel helicopter in 1991. It flew from Invercargill to Campbell Island to evaluate a system for the emergency evacuation of Metservice staff then working at Campbell. Fuel-storage depots have been set up at Enderby Island in the Auckland group and at Campbell Island.

Helicopter flights to evacuate people seriously ill or injured on fishing vessels in subantarctic waters are now reasonably common. Helicopters were used extensively for the Campbell Island rat eradication project in 2001.

Royal New Zealand Air Force long-range aircraft fly 'deep patrols' for fisheries surveillance in the subantarctic region and have been used in the past for albatross monitoring through aerial photography.

Eastern rockhopper penguins at their nest site at Chambres Inlet, Auckland Island, dwarfed by the megaherbs *Stilbocarpa polaris* and *Anisotome latifolia*. TUI DE ROY

boundaries – the Antarctic and Subtropical Convergences – are scattered like knucklebones across the Southern Ocean as if sent sprawling by a clumsy geological hand.

For clues to the age and origins of these islands you need to look to the seabed. The islands are the protruding high points of huge underwater tablelands known as the Campbell Plateau and Bounty Platform – extensions of the continental shelf around mainland New Zealand. These shelf areas bulge south and east of mainland New Zealand, providing relatively shallow water for marine life. The western trio of The Snares, Auckland and Campbell Islands are perched on the Campbell Plateau; the Bounty and Antipodes Islands are lined up to the east on the Bounty Platform. The edges of the Campbell Plateau and Bounty Platform are typically steep and they fall away to abyssal depths. The Antipodes group, at the edge of the Bounty Platform, is only a few kilometres from ocean that is several thousand metres deep.

A splash of herbal colour amid the tussock grassland of Adams Island: from left, the yellow-flowering Macquarie Island cabbage *Stilbocarpa polaris*, the daisy *Pleurophyllum criniferum* and the bright pink flowers of an endemic gentian species. KATH WALKER

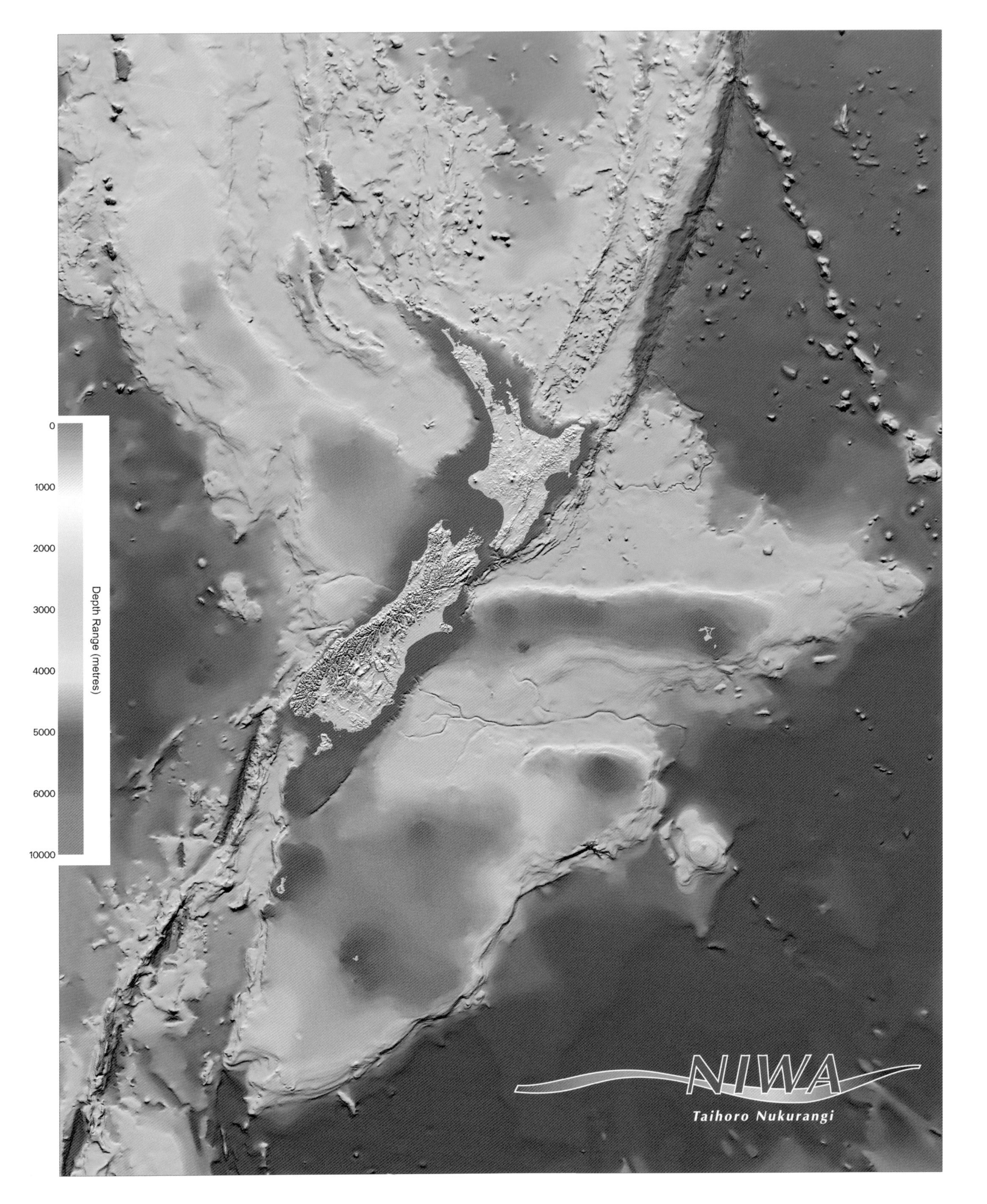
0
1000
2000
3000
4000
5000
6000
10000
Depth Range (metres)
NIWA
Taihoro Nukurangi

Rocky fellfield environment on the summit crest at the southern end of Auckland Island, near Wilkes Peak (580 m). BRIAN RANCE

In keeping with the biological diversity of the region, the geological history is also varied and fascinating. The northernmost groups (The Snares and Bounty Islands) are chips off the old block. They are made of the parent seabed rocks: granite and metamorphic rocks more than 100 million years old. In the case of the Bounty Islands, only stark granite tips are showing. The other three groups are of quite different construction. They are volcanic and much younger. The Auckland Islands represent the eroded remains of a volcano that erupted progressively between 25 and 10 million years ago. Campbell Island's hilly terrain developed from volcanic activity eleven to six million years ago, and the Antipodes group, youngest of all, began to form five million years ago. The last volcanic activity was less than a million years ago.

The volcanism in this region progressed in an eastwards direction as the crustal plate passed over a hot zone in the earth's mantle, with magma popping to the surface as it travelled. The volcanism built islands lofty and large enough, in the case of the Auckland and Campbell groups, to support glaciation during the ice ages of the past two million years. In these two groups are glacial features such as cirques, glaciated valleys, fiords and moraines. But no glaciers or icefields remain today. Snow is reasonably common in winter and spring but does not usually lie for more than a few days. All islands except the Bounty group have thick layers of peat, which is sustained by a moist, cool climate.

Today the New Zealand subantarctic region lies close to a significant plate boundary: a 'triple junction' in fact. Near here is the junction of the Pacific, Australian and Antarctic Plates. Long ago, the splitting and movement of these plates – part of the breakup of the ancient southern super-continent of Gondwana – created the circumpolar Southern Ocean, now surrounded by a jigsaw of continents and islands. This crustal rearrangement explains why the granite islands of The Snares and Bounty groups are similar to the rocks of Fiordland and Antarctica's Marie Byrd Land.

Rock fortress: columnar basalt forms a wall straight out of the sea at Smoothwater Bay, Campbell Island. TUI DE ROY

Bathymetry map opposite: UNDERSEA NEW ZEALAND. The five groups of subantarctic islands are perched on continental crust that extends south and east of mainland New Zealand – part of a submerged mini-continemt coloured red, orange and yellow. Between the Campbell Plateau/ Bounty Platform region in the south and the Chatham Rise extending off the Canterbury coast is a huge undersea valley. The ocean floor beyond the continental crust drops to abyssal depths of 4,000 to 6,000 metres. Courtesy of the National Institute of Water and Atmospheric research. Copyright NIWA

First to map the groups

HOW IRONIC that an expedition seeking tropical breadfruit would be the first to map a New Zealand subantarctic island group. The year was 1788, and the expedition that of Captain William Bligh in *HMS Bounty*.

Passing to the south of New Zealand, the Bounty was on her way to Tahiti under orders from the British Government to collect Tahitian breadfruit trees for transfer to the West Indies. On 9 September, just nineteen years after James Cook's momentous first voyage to New Zealand, Bligh recorded 'a cluster of small rocky islands' which he named the 'Bounty Isles' after his ship. The Bounty sailed on to its infamous date with mutiny in the South Pacific islands.

European discovery of the five groups spanned 22 years: 1788 to 1810. Southern Maori, however, visited at least two of the groups – The Snares/Tini Heke and Auckland Islands/Maungahuka or Motu Maha – before they appeared on European maps

Traditional knowledge of islands to the south of Stewart Island/Rakiura has been confirmed in recent times by archaeological discoveries in The Snares and the Auckland Islands, centred on Enderby Island. An ancient adze, manufactured several hundred years ago, was found at The Snares, and rata and *Dracophyllum* (grass tree) charcoal from Sandy Bay on Enderby Island is older than 600 years according to radio-carbon dating.

After the Bounty Islands, the second group to be put on European maps, The Snares, was recorded in November 1791 by another British naval expedition, led by Captain George Vancouver in *HMS Discovery*. Bound for America's northwest coast by way of the Southern Ocean's west winds, the *Discovery* encountered 'a cluster of seven craggy islands', which Vancouver named The Snares out of respect for their potential to wreck vessels sailing too close to them.

In 1800, *HMS Reliance*, returning to England from Sydney in the command of Captain Henry Waterhouse, encountered a group of islands described as 'desolate, Mountainous and barren'. They were close enough to the antipodes – the diametric opposite location on the earth of London – for Captain Waterhouse to call them the Penantipodes.

Six years later, in 1806, an English whaling vessel, the *Ocean*, found the Auckland Islands, which her captain, Abraham Bristow, named in honour of Lord Auckland ('my friend through my father'). An expedition exploring new sealing grounds found the last of the groups, Campbell Island, on 4 January 1810. Captain Frederick Hasselburgh, of the vessel *Perseverance*, named the main island after a Sydney sealing company, Robert Campbell and Co.

Ten times the size of the United States, the Southern Ocean embodies the southern expanses of the Pacific, Atlantic and Indian Oceans. The breakthrough to create the circumpolar sea occurred about 55 million years ago, when a gap opened between South America and Antarctica. This vast new ocean, swirling with the earth's rotation, allowed marine life, including seabirds, whales, dolphins and seals, to flourish amid expanded food webs.

The west-to-east circulation of water masses and currents is known as the West Wind Drift. In the New Zealand sub-antarctic region currents of colder water from the south and warmer water from the north mix or jostle in layers that are differentiated by temperature and salinity. Upwellings of cold water flood the Campbell Plateau from the west, carrying nutrients from deep down that feed the marine ecosystem in the vicinity of the islands.

Sea surface temperatures range from a summer monthly mean of 12°C at The Snares to 5.5°C in the winter months at Campbell Island.

Between primary elements of the marine ecosystem such as krill and phytoplankton and high-order fauna such as whales, seals and seabirds, there are fish in huge numbers. Their economic value to New Zealand is underlined by the presence of fleets of distant-nation deep-sea fishing vessels in the subantarctic seas, especially in the waters over the Campbell Plateau. Thanks to the wide spacing of the five subantarctic island groups, New Zealand has a 200-nautical-mile (370 km) exclusive economic zone that is the fourth largest in the world. It covers 430 million hectares – more than 15 times the land area of New Zealand. (See map on page 6.) New Zealand's subantarctic seas contain a vast amount of biota, and surveys continue to reveal surprising new forms. Eighty percent of the country's biodiversity is found in the sea.

As for the islands themselves, their true value as biodiversity reservoirs has hit home in recent decades, with the creation of the Department of Conservation bringing a commitment to eradicate the introduced animals that have caused havoc to the basic nature of the larger islands in the region.

Sheep, rabbits, cattle, goats, cats and rats, on Campbell, Auckland and Enderby Islands have been the subject of all-or-nothing eradication projects. Note that, unlike many similar mainland projects, eradication is the goal, not control. The eradication work is giving several of the larger islands in the region a new lease of life.

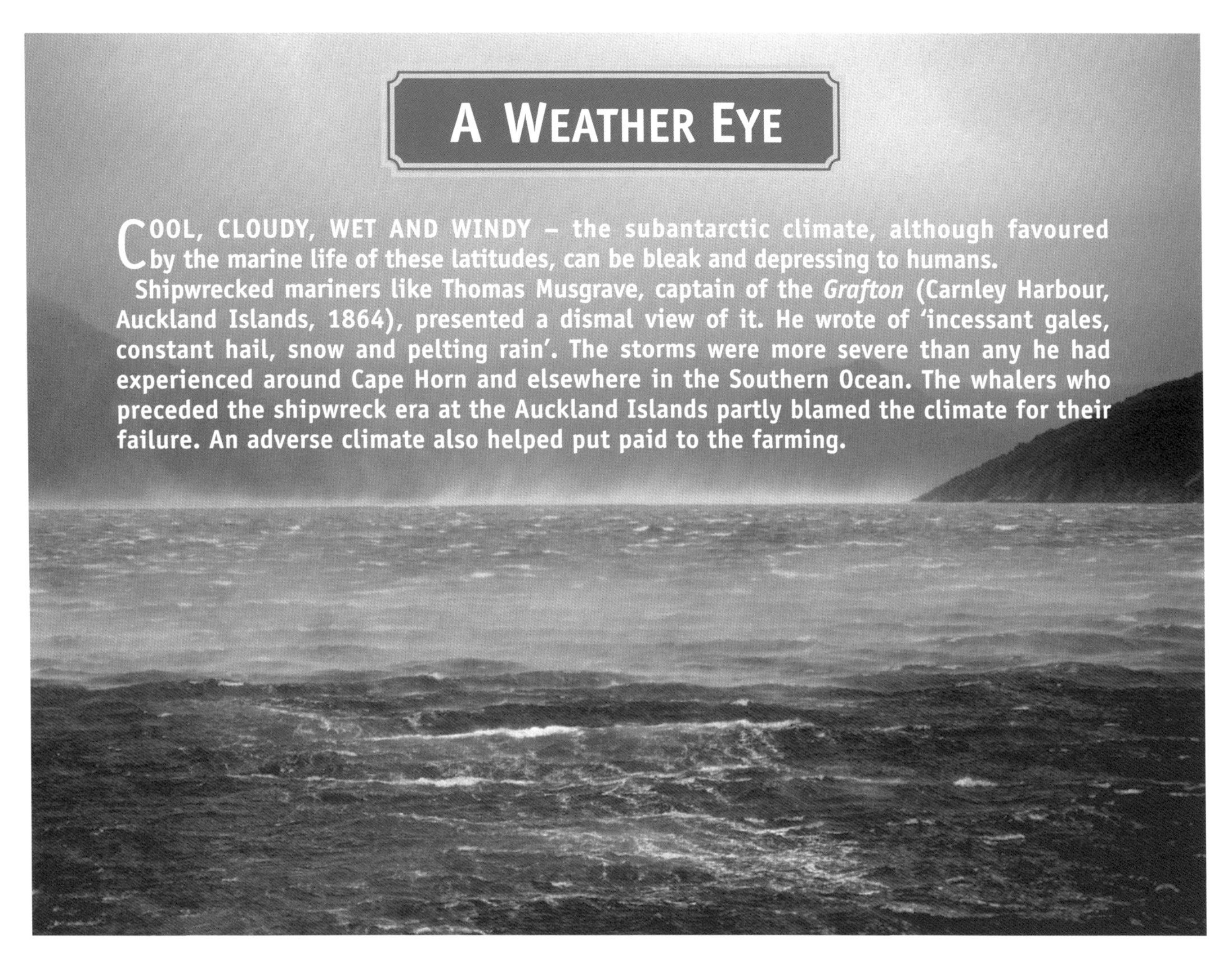

A Weather Eye

COOL, CLOUDY, WET AND WINDY – the subantarctic climate, although favoured by the marine life of these latitudes, can be bleak and depressing to humans.

Shipwrecked mariners like Thomas Musgrave, captain of the *Grafton* (Carnley Harbour, Auckland Islands, 1864), presented a dismal view of it. He wrote of 'incessant gales, constant hail, snow and pelting rain'. The storms were more severe than any he had experienced around Cape Horn and elsewhere in the Southern Ocean. The whalers who preceded the shipwreck era at the Auckland Islands partly blamed the climate for their failure. An adverse climate also helped put paid to the farming.

Spume flies on Campbell Island's Perseverance Harbour in a howling westerly. KIM WESTERSKOV

Today the subantarctic's reputation for foul weather remains, despite the fact there are sometimes successive days, if not a week, of fine conditions. Moist, westerly low-pressure systems radiate out of the 'Furious Fifties' ocean to the south of the islands, battering their rocky western margins and keeping the plant life wind-shorn and hunkered down.

Campbell Island, the most southerly group, cops the roughest weather. Gusts over 50 knots (96 kph), a severe gale, occur on at least 100 days a year, with 35 knots (63 kph) expected on 280 days, three quarters of the year. The westerly airstreams build a persistent westerly swell, with waves reaching phenomenal heights during the wildest storms – as high as 25 metres!

Rain or snow can fall on 300 days of the year, although total annual rainfall at Campbell is not a lot more than Auckland's. Sunshine hours, at little more than 600 a year, reflect the island's cloudy nature (Invercargill expects 1,600 hours).

Campbell is also the coolest of the five New Zealand groups, with a mean annual temperature of about 6°C. This rises to 11°C at The Snares. Because of their isolation and the minimal human 'ecological footprints', the islands offer a good opportunity for researchers to study the effects of climate change.

The geometrid moth *Asaphodes oxyptera* is endemic to the Auckland Islands. Although the female (pictured) has wings, she is flightless and must crawl through herbfields, carefully placing her eggs on larval host herbs.
BRIAN PATRICK

A special set of insects

LIKE THE SEABIRDS, marine mammals and plants, the insects and other invertebrates of the New Zealand subantarctic region assert a character rather different from their mainland relatives. Many insect species are smaller than their mainland counterparts, and flightlessness is surprisingly common in invertebrate groups that are elsewhere usually flighted.

Many species are found nowhere else. Endemic weta, for example, occur at all five island groups and the seven known stoner (stonefly) species – four at the Auckland Islands, two at Campbell Island and one at The Snares – are also endemic to their island group. Among the moths and butterflies of the region, 36 endemics have been identified in a total of 78 indigenous taxa.

Forty percent of the 275 insect species described from Campbell Island are considered endemic. Rat predation and browsing by sheep have had an impact on insect communities on the island in the past. The large weevil *Oclandius laeviusculus*, 25 mm long, survives only on rat-free small islands adjacent to the main island.

Biogeographers postulate that the endemic invertebrate fauna evolved at a time when the Campbell Plateau was dry land.

All of the pest animals (except for the accidentally introduced rats at Campbell Island and mice at Auckland and Antipodes Islands) were brought to the islands long ago as valuable resources – valuable to castaways, early expeditions and farming. Today no one lives at the islands, shipwrecks are rare, castaway depots unnecessary, and farming has long since been abandoned. The islands are given over to scientific research, conservation management and tourism.

Human endeavour in the New Zealand subantarctic islands, spanning over 200 years, has taken on a fabled aura built upon stories of hardship, sacrifice, stoicism and heroism. Following the voyages of discovery, including those of Maori, there came the sealers and whalers, pathfinding scientists, Maori and Moriori settlers, shipwreck victims, farmers, wartime coastwatchers and in more recent times, weather watchers … a passing parade that represents a tremendous catalogue of drama and intrigue.

French blue rabbit, Enderby Island.
BRIAN AHERN

But in the end, nature is in charge, not humans. As the region's World Heritage nomination asserted:

'Natural beauty here can depend on the angle of sunlight, the clarity of the humid atmosphere, and the mood of the sea, which may be pulverising exposed bluffs on one side of an island while lying unruffled and mirror-like in a fiord on the other side. Gale-force winds may make waterfalls "smoke" and run uphill on towering cliffs or a mass flowering of megaherbs can transform an otherwise grey day into one shot through with exquisite colours. There are days when these islands are enveloped in an unsurpassed bleakness and days of bright blue clarity when they are the most invigorating and wild places on earth'.

The five groups, individually and collectively, are in a world of their own.

After the storm: the western volcanic cliffs of Enderby Island. How big was the wave that deposited the frond of bull kelp (lower right) on the clifftop 30 metres above the sea?
NEVILLE PEAT

Below: Morning sun highlights a waterfall plunging from a hanging valley into rata forest at the head of McLennan Inlet on the east coast of Auckland Island. TUI DE ROY

The Southern Ocean

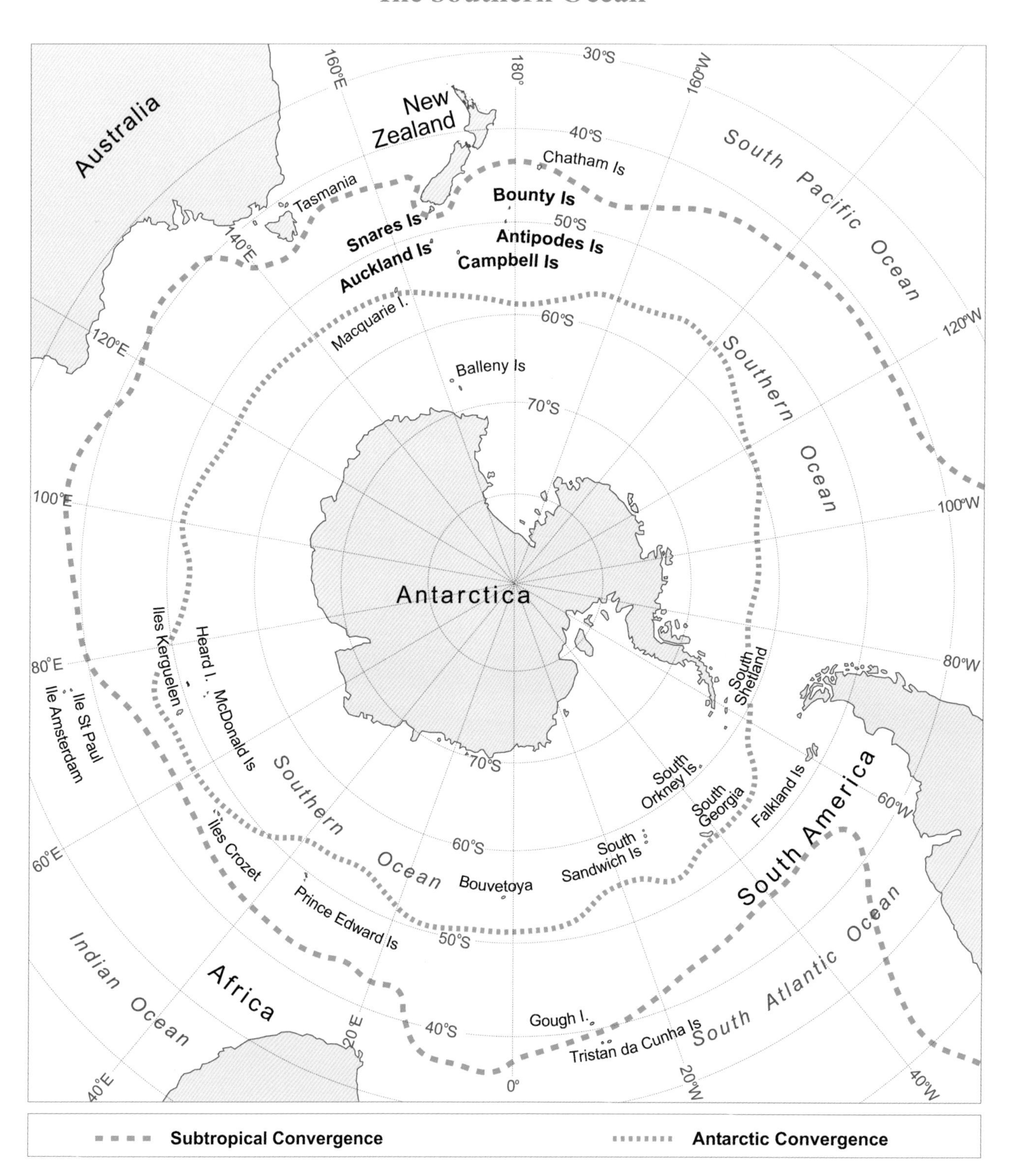

The Five Groups

A geophysical and natural survey

THE NEW ZEALAND subantarctic region is defined by an oceanic boundary or front called the Subtropical Convergence, where subantarctic surface water meets warmer water emanating from the north. This boundary is circumpolar – a lasso meandering through the Southern Ocean largely between 40 degrees and 50 degrees south – and in New Zealand waters it loops between Stewart Island and The Snares. Although ecological mapping makes little distinction between southern Stewart Island and The Snares, the latter is placed with the other four groups making up the New Zealand subantarctic islands.

How different these groups are from one another. At one extreme is the cluster of stark spray-swept islets called the Bounty Islands; at the other the Auckland Islands, looming large out of the misty ocean, a bulwark to the westerly gales. In total, the land area of the five groups is only just over half that of Stewart Island.

Yet the five groups are significant internationally. They are among 22 major oceanic islands or groups of islands spread around the Southern Ocean, representing about 800 individual islands under the jurisdiction of six nations. The contribution of the New Zealand quintet to the biodiversity of the Southern Ocean is out of all proportion to their size.

With the aid of a comparatively mild climate and a productive ocean environment, the New Zealand groups support an assemblage of marine and terrestrial species that is decidedly rich compared to most other subantarctic groups.

Starting with the nearest and northernmost, the five groups are presented in the pages following.

Sunlight bursts through a cloudy day on the east coast of the Auckland Islands.
ANDRIS APSE

THE SNARES / TINI HEKE

THE CLOSEST GROUP to mainland New Zealand, and the most hospitable, The Snares are about 100 km southwest of Stewart Island – just half a day's sailing. There are two clusters: a main group featuring North East Island (280 ha) and adjacent Broughton Island (48 ha), and a line of small islands called the Western Chain, 3.5 km southwest of the main cluster. The highest point (152 m) is on North East Island.

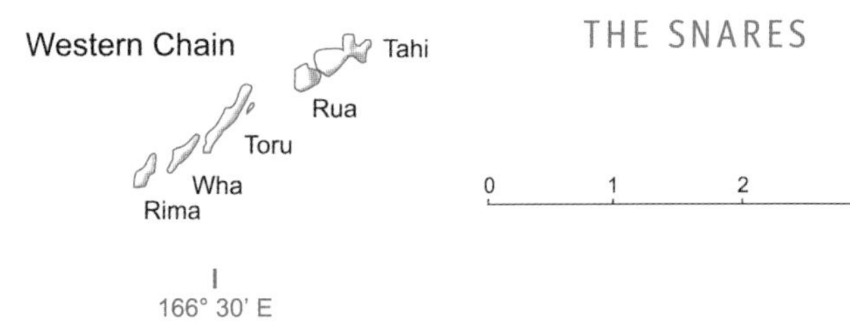

A Snares Island snipe wading through a bed of *Crassula moschata*. ROD MORRIS

Among the islands of the Southern Ocean, The Snares has the distinction of being the only forested group without introduced mammals, not even mice. As such, it is a remarkable haven for wildlife. Granite cliffs surround the bulk of the group, and erosion by the sea has produced deep narrow caverns, sink holes and gulches. These islands are composed of 100 million-year-old Cretaceous muscovite granite, probably part of a large batholith. Crystals of white mica and muscovite are exposed on the cliffs, shore platforms and rock domes that protrude through thick layers of peat.

Lying close to the Subtropical Convergence, The Snares group enjoys a climate that is surprisingly uniform throughout the year. The mean annual temperature is 11°C, and rainfall about 1,200 mm a year.

Snares flora

Forests of the large tree daisy *Olearia lyallii* are the dominant feature across about 80 percent of the main island, forming a canopy over five metres tall in places. These islands are its stronghold. Beneath the canopy the trunks are typically gnarled and bent over by the wind. Another tree daisy, *Brachyglottis stewartiae*, which also occurs on Stewart Island and Foveaux Strait islands, is closely associated with the *Olearia* at The Snares. Elsewhere in the Southern Ocean, the only other islands where tree daisies dominate the vegetation are the Juan Fernandes Islands off the coast of Chile.

The shore hebe, *Hebe elliptica*, common on the mainland, forms dense shrubland at the forest margins and over abandoned penguin colonies. The Snares form of this hebe has larger leaves than the mainland shrub. Prominent under the canopy and in the gullies are the ferns *Polystichum vestitum*, *Blechnum durum* and *Asplenium obtusatum*. Where grasslands hold sway, the large tussock-forming *Poa tennantiana* and the shorter silver tussock *P. astonii* are the main components.

Cook's scurvy grass *Lepidium oleraceum*.
BRIAN RANCE

Among the herbs are three significant species. *Stilbocarpa robusta*, a megaherb with rhubarb-like leaves, is conspicuous in open and bird-manured areas. The only other place it grows is on an island in Foveaux Strait, between Stewart Island/Rakiura and the South Island. Another rare megaherb is *Anisotome acutifolia*, a member of the carrot family. It is found only at The Snares, where it reaches a height of about two metres. The third significant herb is a form of Cook's scurvy grass *Lepidium oleraceum*, which is not a grass at all but a cress. The mainland *Lepidium*, now a threatened plant, was used on Captain James Cook's expeditions to prevent scurvy developing among his crew.

Of the 22 vascular plants found on The Snares, 20 are indigenous. The only introduced plants are the chickweed *Stellaria media* and an annual grass *Poa annua*, neither of which are thought to threaten the flora of The Snares. Besides the vascular plants at The Snares, there are 77 moss and other bryophyte species, 45 lichens and at least six fungi.

The Snares' seaweed communities reflect their proximity to mainland New Zealand. Thirty-two species, in a total of 114, are not recorded from any other subantarctic group but most occur in southern New Zealand.

Sitting pretty: a Buller's mollymawk at its pedestal nest on The Snares, surrounded by the large tree daisy *Olearia lyallii*, the rhubarb-like leaves of *Stilbocarpa robusta* and the coastal shrub *Hebe elliptica*. In the distance is South Promontory and Broughton Island.
ANDRIS APSE

Between spring and autumn, the breeding season, the sky over The Snares fills with sooty shearwaters/titi returning to their burrows for the night – an extraordinary wildlife phenomenon. The birds that have burrows under the forest canopy will crash through the trees to reach them.
DARREN SCOTT

Snares fauna

Seabirds make the most of The Snares for breeding and resting. It is a seabird city, with high-density occupation across almost all suitable habitats. Shearwaters, petrels and penguins are abundant. Curiously, the Western Chain of small, barely-vegetated islands supports an assemblage of seabirds similar to that of the non-vegetated Bounty Islands, 940 km to the east.

The sooty shearwater or titi *Puffinus griseus* is the most numerous, with a couple of million arriving in the spring for the summer breeding season from winter quarters in the North Pacific. The peat layer is honeycombed with their burrows, to which they return en masse at dusk, crashing through the canopy or scrambling madly over the forest floor. At dawn, when they set out for fishing grounds again, they darken the skies over the islands – a phenomenal sight. Although these shearwaters also breed in South America and Australia, The Snares and Stewart Island/Rakiura are strongholds, with The Snares possibly having the largest population of any island.

Titi Studies

RENOWNED FOR ITS ENERGETIC FLYING STYLE, the sooty shearwater or titi *Puffinus griseus* is also agile under water. In pursuit of fish, it can dive, wing-propelled, to an incredible 65 metres.

Studies of these birds by University of Otago zoology researchers have shown that titi commonly dive to such depths in pursuit of prey, with most dives occurring during daylight hours. Feeding trips away from their colonies last up to 14 days. Prey includes fish, squid and crustaceans – up to 37 species.

Rakiura Maori have engaged the Otago University scientists to assess harvesting impacts on the titi population in a co-managed project titled Kia Mau Te Titi Mo Ake Tonu Atu (Keep the Titi Forever), begun in 1996. The project's overall goal is to measure whether current harvesting is sustainable. At The Snares, which supports the largest non-harvested titi population in the New Zealand region, research has focussed on titi population dynamics and foraging behaviour. Following centuries of tradition, titi are harvested by Rakiura Maori on the Titi Islands off Stewart Island/Rakiura. Only the fledglings are harvested, during April and May, and they are marketed as muttonbirds.

Sadly, the study has confirmed a significant decline in the breeding population at The Snares. This finding is consistent with American research identifying a 90 percent decline in the number of titi flying past California on their way south.

From a breeding population at The Snares estimated in 1971 at 2.75 million pairs, there has been a decline of 37 percent or just on one million pairs over about 30 years. The new estimate is based on active burrow counts across the main island. The researchers used a 'burrowscope' fitted with an infra-red camera to determine occupancy. They were amazed by the complexity of many of the burrows, which were more vertically layered than those at Stewart Island/Rakiura. One burrow looked like an 'apartment block'.

Possible reasons for the decline include changes in sea surface temperatures and food supply caused by climate change. The El Nino weather pattern, which causes warm water to move back to the eastern side of the Pacific and cover the cold current welling up from the deep, has been linked to sooty shearwater productivity. The El Nino phenomenon was prominent through the 1990s. Researchers also point to a massive driftnet bycatch as a reason for the population decline. Several million titi were killed between 1978 and 1991.

Nonetheless, sooty shearwaters are still the most abundant seabirds in the Southern Hemisphere. They are long-lived birds, with many reaching over 30 years of age.

An adult sooty shearwater rests on the peat layer beneath the forest canopy after a day at sea fishing. DARREN SCOTT

The most numerous seabird here after the sooty shearwater is probably the common diving petrel *Pelecanoides urinatrix*, small stocky birds that nest in burrows and raise one chick a season. They dive for krill, using their wings for propulsion. The mottled petrel *Pterodroma inexpectata*, an endemic New Zealand species, has a significant breeding population at The Snares, where the southernmost colonies are found. The Snares cape pigeon, generally a smaller race than the circumpolar cape pigeon, has its main breeding base at these islands, with smaller numbers utilising the other New Zealand subantarctic groups. Also breeding at The Snares are broad-billed prion, fairy prion, the rarer fulmar prion and brown skua.

Four albatross species are listed as breeding at The Snares but only two are consistent breeders. Of these two species, the more numerous is the southern Buller's mollymawk *Thalassarche bulleri bulleri*, with about 8,700 pairs. They breed on North East Island, Broughton Island and Alert Stack off the southwest tip of the main island. Solander

Island in Foveaux Strait is the only other breeding base for this species. The Western Chain harbour colonies of Salvin's mollymawk *Thalassarche salvini*, probably fewer than 700 pairs. Their main breeding ground is at the Bounty Islands. A few black-browed mollymawk *T. melanophrys* have bred at The Snares in the past and one nest of Chatham albatross *T. eremita* was found in the Western Chain in 1995.

After the sooty shearwater, the bird most closely associated with The Snares is the Snares crested penguin *Eudyptes robustus*. They typically gather in groups under the tree daisies and sometimes perch on the bent-over trunks. Breeding only at The Snares, these penguins have established more than 100 colonies on the larger islands of the group. Their colonies kill the vegetation but it re-establishes when the penguins move to a new site.

Three land birds are endemic to The Snares: the Snares Island fernbird *Bowdleria punctata caudata*, the insect-eating Snares Island tomtit *Petroica macrocephala dannefaerdi*, and the less conspicuous Snares Island snipe *Coenocorypha huegeli*, which is partly nocturnal. The fernbird, the most numerous, likes to forage near the ground, especially around penguin colonies. Fernbird density of eight pairs per hectare has been calculated. The tomtit population is conservatively estimated at 500 breeding pairs.

Perching penguins: Snares crested penguins have the unusual (for penguins) habit of perching on the horizontal branches of *Olearia* trees. DARREN SCOTT

A Snares Island tomtit. TUI DE ROY

Buller's Benefit

ALTHOUGH THEY DO GET CAUGHT by fishing gear, southern Buller's albatrosses also benefit from commercial deep-sea fishing activities. A study of the diet of these birds, based on what they are feeding their chicks, shows that fish discarded by deep-water trawlers comprise 91 percent of the weight of all fish consumed by the birds and 60 percent of the diet by weight.

Between 1969 and 1992, Buller's albatross numbers at The Snares increased by 78 percent, and they increased a further 8 percent in the five years to 1997. The Snares population is estimated at 8,700 pairs. The increase is probably due in part to the extra food supply available from discards from fishing vessels. Jack mackerel, hoki and javelin fish – all fish ordinarily unavailable to the albatrosses – were the main species identified in the study. (The Solander Islands population has been in decline in recent years, however, as a result of birds being caught in fishing gear.)

Buller's albatrosses raise one chick a year and they are long-lived (a banded bird was at least 53 years old when it disappeared). Studies by NIWA scientists of their foraging behaviour in the 1990s, using satellite telemetry, show that they are able to fly long distances to feed – as far as the east coast of Tasmania and Chile. They also forage off the east coast of the South Island.

Snares crested penguins swimming near their colony.
KIM WESTERSKOV

Other indigenous land birds breeding at The Snares and common on the mainland are silvereye and grey warbler. South Island fantail arrived at The Snares between 1977 and 1981, flourished briefly on the main island, but are no longer present. Swampy areas attract the native grey duck and introduced mallard. Other introduced species include redpoll, chaffinch, blackbird, starling, house sparrow and song thrush, although their numbers remain low compared to the indigenous birds.

Around the coastline, the New Zealand fur seal *Arctocephalus forsteri* and New Zealand sea lion *Phocarctos hookeri* are breeding. The fur seals were all but wiped out by sealing operations 200 years ago but they have made a comeback and now number more than 1,000 adults. The sea lions are in much smaller numbers.

The terrestrial invertebrates include several endemic beetles, land snails and worms.

Possibly Southern New Zealand's most endangered beetle is the Broughton Island weevil *Lyperobius nesidiotes*, which is restricted to a small area on Broughton Island.

One worm grows to a length of 200 mm. The large weevil *Hadramphus stilbocarpae*, which here feeds on the megaherb *Stilbocarpa robusta*, reaches its southern limit at The Snares, as do some beetles and moths.

The knobbled weevil, *Hadramphus stilbocarpae*, inhabits The Snares group. MIKE MEADS

A cave weta, *Insulanaplectron spinosum*, from The Snares group. MIKE MEADS

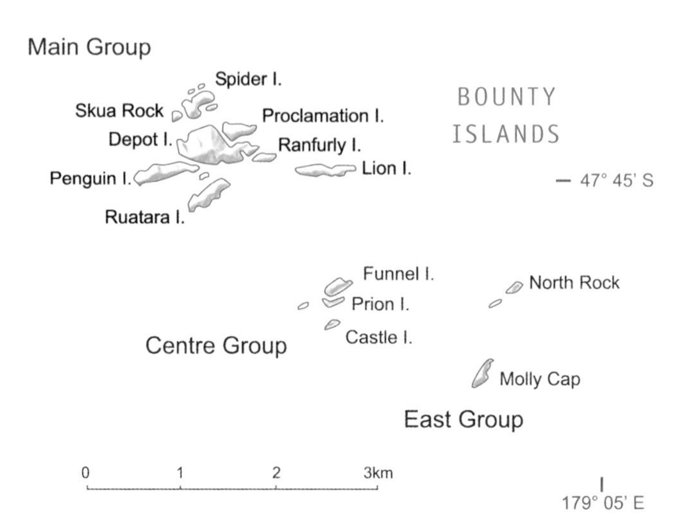

BOUNTY ISLANDS

When *HMS Bounty* sailed past these islands in 1788, Captain William Bligh recorded 'white spots like patches of snow'. What he observed was almost certainly not snow but areas of guano deposited by generations of seabirds and enamelled to the granite surfaces.

A more graphic symbol of the sea's dominance over land in these latitudes would be hard to imagine. The Bounty Islands resemble the last vestiges of a disappearing landmass – the tips of the submerged Bounty Platform. The 20 small, low islands, 135 ha all up, form three groups called Main, Centre and East. Part of the Main Group, 800 m-long Depot Island is the largest. With the highest point just 88 m above the sea, a severe storm will cover the entire group in salt spray. The Bounty Islands are rarely visited by scientists or anyone else. Remoteness and the lack of safe anchorages are off-putting. In any case, permits are required for landings because of the vulnerable nature of the wildlife and the risks posed by the inadvertent introduction of pests. Scientists coming ashore here are warned about the polished, slippery surfaces, and some will resort to wearing woollen socks over their boots for safety.

The northernmost of the five subantarctic groups, the Bounty Islands lie 940 km east of The Snares and 700 km from the South Island. The nearest islands are the Antipodes, 220 km due south. The Bounty Islands comprise smooth outcrops of granite of early Jurassic age, about 180 million years old and more closely related to the Jurassic granite of West Antarctica than to New Zealand rocks. Some cliff faces feature columnar jointing, and the summit rocks are angular.

The Bounty Islands are mere specks in a boundless ocean, crowded with marine life. In the scene below, Salvin's mollymawks and erect-crested penguins are prominent. TUI DE ROY

There is virtually no soil development on the Bounty Islands. The higher islands carry a film of hard polished guano but elsewhere winter rains tend to wash away the bird droppings from the previous summer. Hollows become filled with brown organic sludge formed from decaying carcasses, moulted penguin feathers, excreta, food scraps and seaweed washed up by waves or brought ashore by the Bounty Island shags as nesting material.

At the Bounty Islands the common bull kelp *Durvillaea antarctica*, which creates a continuous swirling fringe around the shoreline, is mostly a striking golden colour instead of the usual dark brown – apparently a response to bleaching under sunlight and clear water conditions.

Weather information is sparse. A mean annual temperature of 10°C is an estimate.

Bounty Islands fauna

The Bounty Islands are home to an extraordinarily diverse collection of seabirds and seals that appear to be clinging to a latter-day, long-lost Noah's Ark. It is a long way to the next available nesting or resting place.

Seven seabird species breed here, including the Bounty Island shag *Leucocarbo ranfurlyi*, the world's rarest cormorant. A population of 500 to 600 is estimated.

Three of the other six species are endemic to the New Zealand subantarctic region: the erect-crested penguin *Eudyptes sclateri*, Salvin's mollymawk and Snares cape pigeon. Also breeding here are the fulmar prion, *Pachyptila crassirostris crassirostris*, which is found only in the New Zealand subantarctic islands and Heard Island, Antarctic tern and southern black-backed gull. This is the world capital of both Salvin's mollymawk (75,000 pairs estimated to be breeding here) and erect-crested penguins, whose only other breeding site is the Antipodes group.

The Governor and the shag

AN EXPEDITION mounted by an early Governor of New Zealand, the Earl of Ranfurly, discovered the Bounty Island shag, whose scientific name, *Leucocarbo ranfurlyi*, recalls the event. The Governor, responding to a request from the British Museum for specimens of New Zealand birds, set out for the subantarctic islands in the government steamer *Hinemoa* in December 1900. Assisting him was the naturalist Frederick Hutton, curator of Canterbury Museum. The expedition visited all five subantarctic island groups, and the cormorant collected at the Bounty Island acquired the Governor's name.

A glorious underwater environment at the Bounty Islands contrasts with the largely black-and-white world of the islands themselves.
KIM WESTERSKOV

New Zealand fur seals haul out and breed at the Bounty Islands.
KIM WESTERSKOV

Penguins are the most numerous seabirds at the Bounty Islands, and the mollymawks are often interspersed with them – a diving specialist alongside one of the world's most proficient fliers. And on land they both make a lot of noise. Over the sound of waves crashing, they generate a cacophony of honking, trumpeting, braying and cackling at the height of the summer breeding season. Meanwhile, the shags and cape pigeons nest on precipitous ledges and the prions favour crevices and holes. The shags have coped with the lack of terrestrial plant material to build their nests by collecting the brown seaweed *Marginariella* from the sea. They often dive over 15 metres for it. The mollymawks utilise penguin feathers to reinforce their pedestal nests.

Somehow there is room in this seabird city for seals. The New Zealand fur seal *Arctocephalus forsteri* has chosen the tiny Bounty Islands as one of its main bases in the subantarctic. At last count (1992) there were over 20,000 of them. Yet they have still not recovered from near extermination at this site at the hands of 19th century sealers. The first two years of Bounty Islands sealing killed 50,000 seals. By the early 1830s, just a handful were left.

Despite the lack of soil and plant life here, a diverse community of terrestrial invertebrates inhabits the Bounty Islands. Their existence depends on the detritus generated by the seabirds and seals. The insects include a flightless beetle *Bountya insularis*, whose nearest relatives are in Australia and South America. The flightless theme continues through an endemic weta (orthopteran) *Ischyroplectron isolatum* and two moth species – *Proterodesma turbotti* and a new species of *Reductoderces* – which are shared with the Antipodes Islands. Two spiders have been discovered so far: *Pacificana cockayni*, a Bounty Island endemic, and *Rubrius mummosus*, which has South American relatives.

Pastoral pretensions

A SHEEP FARM on the Bounty Islands? That bizarre prospect occurred for a moment in 1895, when the New Zealand Government advertised a pastoral leasehold opportunity there: 'Run No. 513, being the Bounty Islands, containing 335 acres 2 roods; term, twenty-one years'. Someone ignored the fact the islands had no vegetation above the high tide mark!

The only record of an introduced bird is that of a starling, presumably swept here from mainland New Zealand or The Snares in a westerly storm.

Until 2004, terrestrial plant life at the Bounty Islands was restricted to some crustose lichens. Then, in November 2004, a 10-day expedition led by Tui de Roy, Mark Jones and Jacinda Amey discovered Cook's scurvy grass *Lepidium oleraceum* on nelly Cap and Funnel Islands – the group's first vascular plant.

ANTIPODES ISLANDS

PERCHED ON THE SOUTHEAST MARGIN of the Bounty Platform, over 800 km from the South Island, the Antipodes group is the remotest – and also the youngest – of the New Zealand subantarctic islands. At 49° 41' south, the group is more or less diametrically opposite London on the planet, hence the unusual name for the main island. The group comprises a main island, six smaller islands within two kilometres of it, and numerous islets and stacks. Antipodes Island, at 2,025 ha, accounts for 97 percent of the total land area. Of the smaller islands, Bollons (50 ha) is the largest. With adjacent Archway Island it forms a scalloped semi-circle that graphically portrays the remains of an eroded crater now mostly flooded by the sea.

Cliffs up to 150 m high ring the main island and erosion by the sea has left a ragged shoreline dotted with sea caves, stacks and wave-cut platforms. Measuring a chunky seven by five kilometres, Antipodes Island rises to an altitude of 366 m at Mt Galloway. The bulk of the main island is a rough, undulating plateau, dissected by deep alluvial gullies. There are several volcanic cones and craters, with Mt Galloway and Mt Waterhouse, near the centre of the island, the most prominent of the cones. Some of the rocks are less than a million years old, and the oldest are about five million years. Deposits of peat up to five metres deep blanket much of the main island. Basalt boulders mantle the beaches.

Persistent westerly winds buffet the group, and it is often overcast, with drizzle. Annual rainfall is estimated at 1,000–1,500 mm. A mean annual temperature of 8°C is estimated.

Antipodes flora

Dense grasslands predominate. Forest has not developed despite the slightly higher latitude than the Auckland Islands, where rata forest grows. Among the grasses, *Poa litorosa* is the main species, forming pedestal tussocks up to two metres tall on the most favourable sites. Progress on foot through the densest patches is difficult. On the exposed inland plateau areas, it has a lower stature, and near the coast the softer *Poa foliosa* is common. Ferns are often associated with the grassland. Prickly shield fern *Polystichum vestitum* is the commonest, especially on wetter sites.

Only four woody species occur at the Antipodes, all coprosmas. *Coprosma antipoda*, possibly a variety of *C. rugosa*, is an island endemic, growing in patches up to two metres tall. Gullies and other sheltered sites harbour the spectacular *Stilbocarpa polaris* or Macquarie Island cabbage, a megaherb endemic to the New Zealand subantarctic region and Macquarie Island. Other herb species found here include a rare gentian, *Gentiana antipoda*, the daisy *Pleurophyllum criniferum*, which has flowers with no petals, and the carrot relative *Anisotome antipoda*.

Of the 71 vascular plants at the Antipodes, 68 are indigenous and 18 of these are shared with the Auckland and Campbell groups. The three introduced plants are not widespread and probably pose no threat to the indigenous communities.

Of interest to marine algae experts is a new form of bull kelp *Durvillaea antarctica* 'Antipodes Island', which is a massive dark-brown subtidal plant with very thick blades. A new species of brown seaweed *Marginariella* also occurs here.

Antipodes fauna

The magnificent Antipodean wandering albatross *Diomedea antipodensis* is the feature seabird. It nests in the grasslands all over the main island. Except for a handful of nests on Campbell Island, the Antipodes Islands provide the only breeding sites for this species, which was declared a separate species from the other wandering albatrosses of the world in a review of albatross taxonomy in the mid-1990s. Compared to the Gibson's albatross of the Auckland Islands, the Antipodean albatross breeds three weeks later (eggs laid between early January and early February) and has different feeding grounds, east of mainland New Zealand. Female birds are darker at all ages than their Auckland Island relatives.

Antipodes Island is swathed in the large tussock *Poa litorosa*, which reaches two metres in height.
ANDRIS APSE

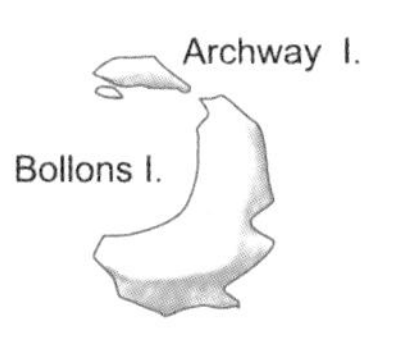

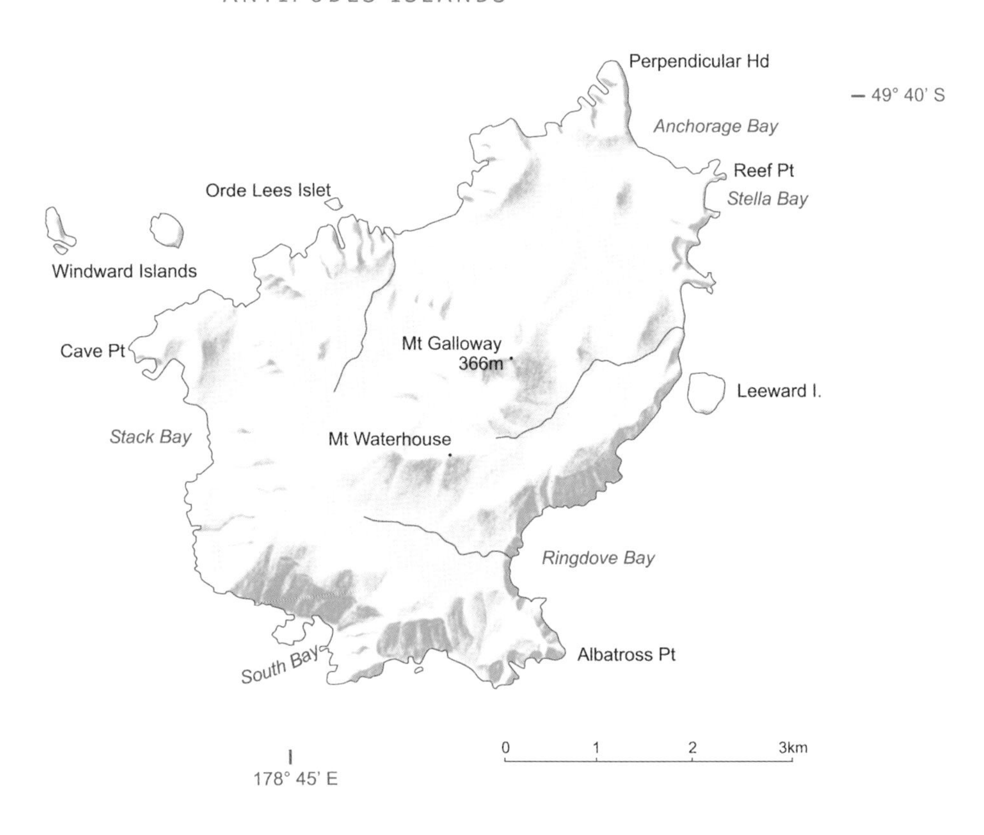

Antipodean Albatross

DOWN BUT NOT OUT, the Antipodean albatross has suffered a substantial decline in numbers as a result of incidental capture by longline fishing vessels.

The bird's main prey is squid, which southern bluefin tuna also pursue, and a bycatch scenario is created when tuna fishing vessels bait their lines with frozen squid. In the 1990s tuna boats reported that Antipodes birds made up a quarter of all wandering albatrosses killed through entanglement in hooks.

Antipodes albatrosses breed every two years and at last count, about 5,000 pairs were breeding each year. Since 1996, satellite transmitters attached temporarily to several albatrosses have been giving researchers information about the foraging flights of these birds, which feed east of the New Zealand mainland.

Three other albatross species breed at the Antipodes in small numbers: light-mantled sooty albatross, black-browed mollymawk and very small numbers of white-capped albatross *Thalassarche steadi*, a New Zealand endemic species.

At the shoreline, penguin colonies are conspicuous. Two species breed here: erect-crested and eastern rockhopper. After the Bounty Islands, the Antipodes group is the main home of the erect-crested penguin *Eudyptes sclateri*. A 1995 census reported a significant decline to about 50,000 nests, half the number counted in 1978. Rockhopper populations have also fallen sharply, with only 3,400 nests reported in 1995.

The Antipodes group is a haven for petrels. It is the only breeding site in the New Zealand subantarctic region for the soft-plumaged petrel *Pterodroma mollis*. The commonest petrel species here is the subantarctic diving petrel *Pelecanoides urinatrix exsul*, a circumpolar species. There are also populations of white-headed, white-chinned, grey and northern giant petrels. Sooty shearwater and fairy prion breed here as well.

Young Antipodean wandering albatrosses socialising at Antipodes Island. TUI DE ROY

Right: Cliffs form much of the Antipodes Island coastline. The gentler slopes allow erect-crested penguins to establish colonies. TUI DE ROY

Stretching her wings, this female Antipodean wandering albatross displays at her nest on the west side of Antipodes Island.
KATH WALKER

A colony of erect-crested penguins, Antipodes Island. ANDRIS APSE

Among the endemic land birds, the Antipodes parakeet *Cyanoramphus unicolor* is special. It evolved in this remote place, a bird of about 130 g and 300 mm long, the largest of the New Zealand parakeets. It is commonly found feeding on tussock leaves in the grassland. It also scavenges around the penguin colonies. A second, smaller parakeet also occurs here. Reischek's parakeet is a subspecies of the mainland New Zealand red-crowned parakeet. Antipodes Island snipe is widespread on Antipodes Island and the larger outliers – a lighter, longer-billed version of the Snares Island snipe. The fourth endemic land bird is the Antipodes Island pipit, which frequents the grasslands and open habitats.

Altogether, 25 birds breed on the Antipodes group. Introduced birds include red poll, dunnock and starling.

New Zealand fur seals appear to be increasing again following near extinction at the Antipodes by 19th century sealers. The first pups were recorded in 1985. The other significant marine mammal of the Antipodes is the southern elephant seal *Mirounga leonina*, which has established about six breeding sites here, producing a total of about 100 pups a year.

Invertebrate species include a range of endemics: nine beetles, a weta, two spiders and four moths. More than a quarter of the 150 insect species here are endemic. Several groups of moth are at their southern limit here, including the common mainland magpie moth. A snail *Kerguelenella flemingi* is thought to be endemic to the Antipodes, Auckland and Campbell Islands.

The Bollons Island insect communities are more diverse and abundant than those on the main island, which are impacted by mice, the main island's only alien mammal.

A Reischek's parakeet on a flowerhead of *Anisotome antipoda*. TUI DE ROY

Erect-crested penguins at the water's edge, Antipodes Island. The bull kelp here is a local variety of widespread *Durvillea antarctica*.
TUI DE ROY

Elephant seals hauled out at Hut Cove, Antipodes Island.
KATH WALKER

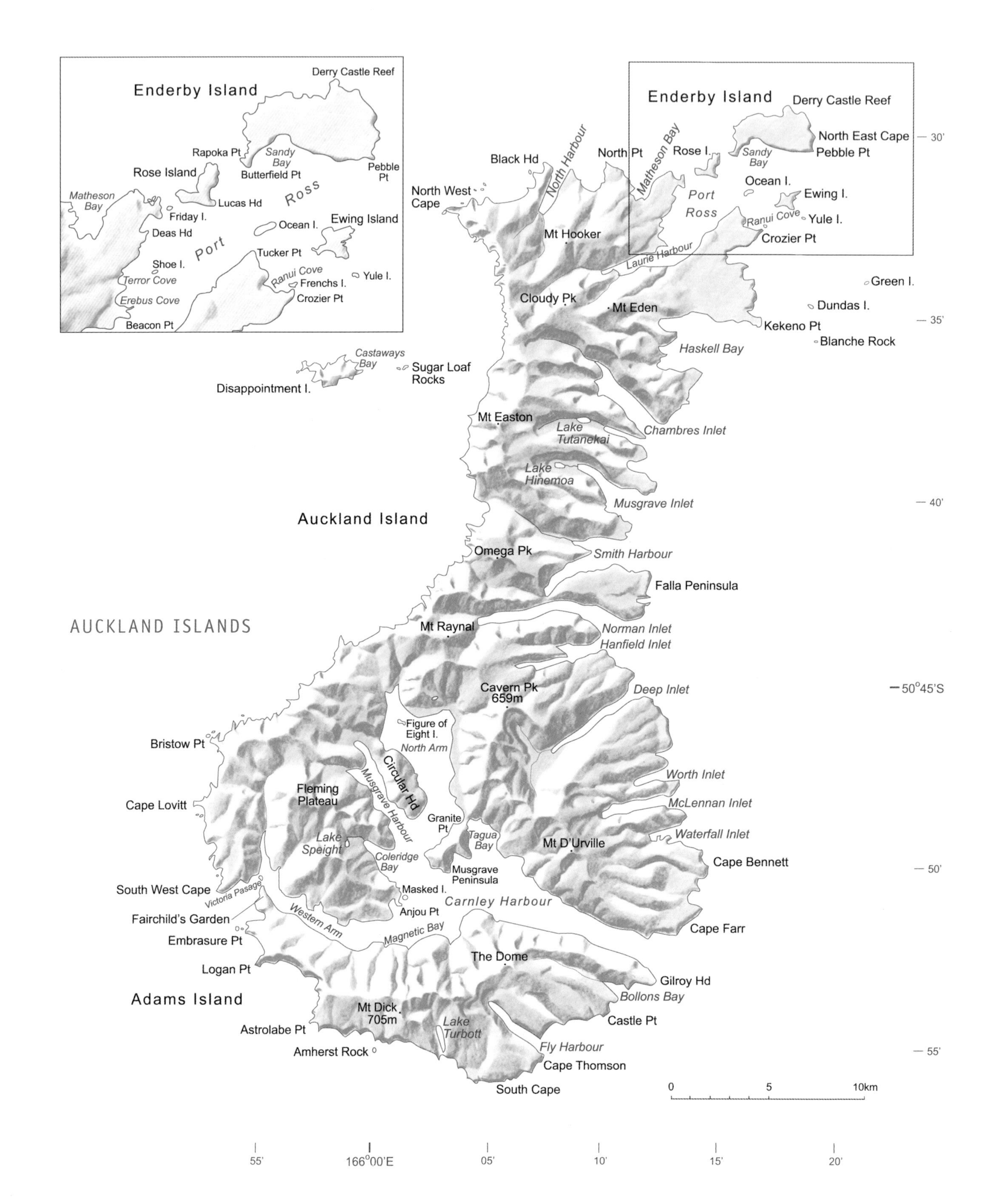
AUCKLAND ISLANDS
Enderby Island
Derry Castle Reef
North East Cape
Pebble Pt
Sandy Bay
Rose I.
Matheson Bay
Port Ross
Ocean I.
Ewing I.
Yule I.
Ranui Cove
Crozier Pt
Rapoka Pt
Butterfield Pt
Rose Island
Lucas Hd
Friday I.
Deas Hd
Ewing Island
Tucker Pt
Shoe I.
Terror Cove
Erebus Cove
Frenchs I.
Beacon Pt
Black Hd
North Harbour
North Pt
North West Cape
Mt Hooker
Laurie Harbour
Green I.
Cloudy Pk
Mt Eden
Dundas I.
Kekeno Pt
Blanche Rock
Haskell Bay
Castaways Bay
Sugar Loaf Rocks
Disappointment I.
Mt Easton
Lake Tutanekai
Chambres Inlet
Lake Hinemoa
Musgrave Inlet
Auckland Island
Omega Pk
Smith Harbour
Falla Peninsula
Mt Raynal
Norman Inlet
Hanfield Inlet
Deep Inlet
Cavern Pk 659m
Figure of Eight I.
North Arm
Bristow Pt
Circular Hd
Musgrave Harbour
Fleming Plateau
Cape Lovitt
Worth Inlet
McLennan Inlet
Waterfall Inlet
Granite Pt
Tagua Bay
Mt D'Urville
Lake Speight
Coleridge Bay
Cape Bennett
Musgrave Peninsula
South West Cape
Victoria Pasage
Masked I.
Carnley Harbour
Anjou Pt
Fairchild's Garden
Western Arm
Magnetic Bay
Embrasure Pt
Cape Farr
The Dome
Logan Pt
Gilroy Hd
Bollons Bay
Adams Island
Mt Dick 705m
Lake Turbott
Castle Pt
Astrolabe Pt
Fly Harbour
Amherst Rock
Cape Thomson
South Cape
0
5
10km
30'
35'
40'
50°45'S
50'
55'
55'
166°00'E
05'
10'
15'
20'

AUCKLAND ISLANDS / MOTU MAHA / MAUNGAHUKA

THE LARGEST, HIGHEST, and biologically the richest of the five groups, the Auckland Islands lie 460 km south of Bluff in latitude 50 degrees south and at the western margin of the Campbell Plateau. The main island, Auckland Island (50,990 ha in area and 40 km long), is large enough to accommodate all the other islands in the New Zealand subantarctic region put together. It widens at its southern end, where Carnley Harbour separates it from Adams Island (10,119 ha), the second largest island in the group. Carnley Harbour, 72 sq km in area, is magnificently spacious. Strictly speaking it is more a strait than a harbour as it is open at both ends, although the western opening is narrow and a dangerous place, especially in storms. In the north, main island headlands and a set of smaller islands create Port Ross. The islands here include Enderby (710 ha), Rose (75 ha) and Ewing (57 ha).

About 6 km off the west coast is Disappointment Island (566 ha). Mt Dick (705 m) on Adams Island is the highest point in the group, with Cavern Peak (659 m) the highest peak on Auckland Island, which is mountainous throughout its length.

What you see now are the eroded and sea-flooded remains of two ancient volcanoes, one centred on Carnley Harbour, the other centred on Disappointment Island. They were formed between 25 and 10 million years ago. Carnley Harbour is a caldera, with Musgrave Peninsula lying at about the centre. The volcanic rocks rest on

Eaten by the sea: eroded volcanic rocks at Bristow Point near the southwest corner of the main Auckland Island. ANDRIS APSE

a basement of coarse-grained biotite granite up to 100 million years old and exposed at Granite Point on Musgrave Peninsula. Disappointment Island, built of hard volcanic rock, marks the centre of a volcano whose western side has crumbled under the sea's assault. The west coast is an almost continuous line of sea-pounded cliffs, reaching heights over 400 m in places. In marked contrast, the east coast is indented by a series of bays and long fiord-like inlets, with the land sloping steadily down to headlands at the open sea. Adams Island protects Carnley Harbour from southerly weather. Carnley's narrow western entrance limits the impact of the westerly swells.

The towering western cliffs of the main island are built of possibly the thickest exposed sequence of lava flows in the New Zealand region. Subsequent volcanic activity in the north built the hills and islands surrounding Port Ross. Glaciation in the past two million years has helped shape the landscape. Glaciers dug out cirques and deepened valleys. They dumped moraine and dammed lakes.

Today's climate is a lot milder. There are snowfalls but snow does not accumulate for long. Most of the 1,000–1,500 mm annual precipitation arrives as showers. The tops are frequently under cloud, and westerly winds are persistent. The mean annual temperature is about 8°C. Summer maximum air temperatures generally range between 10° and 16°C, and the winter range is generally between 4° and 10°C. Enderby Island, low-lying and as far east of the mountains as you can get in the Auckland Islands, usually has the finest, warmest weather.

A forest fit for goblins: the twisted trunks of southern rata trees form an open understorey near Sandy Bay, Enderby Island. In summer, their fallen crimson flowers redden the forest floor. ANDRIS APSE

Auckland Islands flora

The flora of the Auckland Islands is a feast for the eyes. From red-flowering rata coastal forest to the tundra-like tops, through shrubland, grassland and meadows of colourful megaherbs, the plant life is diverse and fascinating. The vascular plant list totals 233, of which 84 percent (196 taxa) are indigenous. Compare this to mainland New Zealand today, where the introduced plant species now outnumber the natives.

An Enderby Island gentian. CHRIS RANCE

At least five plants are unique to the Auckland Islands: two gentians (*Gentiana concinna* and *G. cerina*), the buttercup *Ranunculus subantarcticus* subsp. *subantarcticus*, a plantain *Plantago triantha* and the grass *Poa aucklandica* subsp. *aucklandica*.

Coastal forest, dominated by southern rata *Metrosideros umbellata*, reaches an altitude of 50 metres almost everywhere except in some areas around Port Ross, where the tree daisy *Olearia lyallii* has taken charge. At its southern limit here, the rata forms a compact canopy about half the height of its mainland counterpart and when it sets its crimson flowers en masse in January it is a spectacular sight. In a few sheltered inlets, the rata is mixed with the soft tree fern *Cyathea smithii*, the world's southernmost tree fern – a combination that gives this subantarctic island a subtropical appearance. The presence of the large tree fuchsia *Fuchsia excorticata*, a comparatively recent arrival at Auckland Island (dispersal agent unknown), adds to the warm impression.

The forest grades into shrubland higher up, comprising shrubs of *Dracophyllum*, *Coprosma*, *Myrsine*, *Ozothamnus*, *Pseudopanax* and *Hebe*. Above 300 m, a grassland of the

Adams and Disappointment Islands

A herb garden of the daisy *Pleurophyllum criniferum* and rhubarb-like leaves of *Stilbocarpa polaris* overlooking the southern cliffs of Adams Island. The daisy displays its flowers, without petals, on tall spikes. ANDRIS APSE

FREE OF INTRODUCED ANIMALS, Adams and Disappointment Islands are refuges of world significance for subantarctic flora and fauna.

Adams Island, 20 km long by up to 7 km wide, although farmed for a time in the past, supports a remarkable collection of plants. Fairchild's Garden, at the northwest tip of the island, is a megaherb wonderland. Here, large coastal herbs like the Macquarie Island cabbage *Stilbocarpa polaris* and the carrot relative *Anisotome latifolia* mingle with species such as the daisy *Pleurophyllum speciosum* and lily *Bulbinella rossii*. Adams has all three *Pleurophyllum* species. Fairchild's Garden was named in 1891 after the captain of the government steamship *Hinemoa*, which carried a scientific expedition to the subantarctic.

From its sheltered northern shores on Carnley Harbour to its high ridges and formidable southern cliffs, where gales send the waterfalls 'smoking' skywards, Adams Island has a representative range of forest, shrub and grassland species as well as the herbs. Its birdlife includes the spectacular Gibsons wandering albatross and an array of terrestrial species. The invertebrate community of Adams Island is remarkably intact.

Disappointment Island, 4 km long by up to 1 km wide, is covered in *Poa* grassland and giant herbs, with scattered areas of shrubland, and fellfield around the top of the island. Large numbers of white-capped mollymawks and numerous petrel species breed here.

A big sea meets cliffs at Auckland Island. KIM WESTERSKOV

Enderby Island megaherbs: pink *Anisotome* flowers mingle with a spectacular field of yellow *Bulbinella rossii*, largest member of its genus. CHRIS RANCE

Rocks with attitude: columns of volcanic basalt form this Port Ross headland, fringed with bull kelp and topped by red-flowering rata trees. TUI DE ROY

tussock-forming *Chionochloa antarctica* is interspersed with herbs, including all three species of *Pleurophyllum*, eye-catching daisies. The rosette daisy *Damnamenia vernicosa* is another attractive inter-tussock species. Above 450 m, ground-hugging fellfield vegetation is common, with *Pleurophyllum hookerii* conspicuous.

Much of the flora of the Auckland Islands is growing on peat soils, with deposits of peat up to eight metres thick having accumulated since the retreat of the ice 10,000 years ago.

Auckland Islands fauna

A showcase for subantarctic wildlife, the Auckland Islands harbour a diverse community of marine mammals, seabirds, land birds and invertebrate animals.

The sea lion population is an outstanding feature. This is the home and castle of the New Zealand or Hooker's sea lion *Phocarctos hookeri*, a rare member of the seal family. About 90 percent of breeding occurs at just four sites. Tiny Dundas Island off the east coast is the main one, and there are two on Enderby Island and another at Figure of Eight Island in Carnley Harbour.

Towards summer the boisterous beachmaster sea lions sort out territories on the breeding beaches and gather the females around them. Pups are born, one to each female, in the Christmas-New Year period, and mating occurs a little over a week after the females have given birth. Between feeding trips that range as far as 150 km from home, mothers will suckle their pups over several months. The total population is estimated at 12,000 to 16,000.

The sea lions will wander far into the forest at Enderby Island and even out on to the hummocky moors. It is a surprise to anyone used to the idea that seals belong near water to see the sea lions wandering bear-like through the rata forest. New Zealand fur seals, on the other hand, remain uncommon at these islands.

Another significant marine mammal of the Auckland Islands is the southern right whale *Eubalaena australis*. These whales frequent Port Ross in the winter for calving and mating. Up to 165 were observed on a single day during studies of the whales in the mid-1990s. Port Ross, including its inner waterway, Laurie Harbour, has become the main breeding ground for southern right whales in the Southwest Pacific.

What a far cry this winter scene is from the picture in 1850, when the whalers of the Enderby Settlement at Port Ross encountered too few whales to make a living. By then they had been hunted almost to extinction in this region. A population of between 740 and 1140 is estimated at the beginning of the 21st century.

Underwater ballet: New Zealand sea lions enjoy the turquoise water off Sandy Bay, Enderby Island. TUI DE ROY

A southern right whale calf, with its mother, at Port Ross, the main breeding ground for the species in the New Zealand region.
KIM WESTERSKOV

According to International Whaling Commission estimates in the late 1990s, the total circumpolar southern right whale population is still less than 10 percent of its pre-exploitation size. Moreover, DNA studies of the population breeding at the Auckland Islands indicate that it is genetically distinct from the southwestern Australian population, the nearest of the three other known southern right whale populations. The gene pool of the Auckland Islands whales is reported to be very low, suggesting a loss of genetic diversity from past exploitation.

A few southern elephant seals breed at Dundas Island and individuals haul out to rest elsewhere around the Auckland Islands coastline. Leopard seals occasionally visit from their haunts in Antarctic waters.

Seabirds abound here. Three species are outstanding. These are the Gibson's albatross *Diomedea gibsoni*, a member of the wandering albatross group, the southern royal albatross *Diomedea epomophora* and white-capped albatross *Thalassarche steadi*.

Mutual preening by a pair of white-capped albatrosses, South West Cape, Auckland Island.
TUI DE ROY

Gibson's wandering albatrosses stretch their wings in a courtship display at Adams Island. The displays may include a pirouette with wings outstretched. TUI DE ROY

Gibson's wandering albatross, with a wingspan close to three metres, breeds only at the Auckland Islands and mostly on Adams Island. Like most albatrosses, these birds are long-lived and slow-breeding. They do not start reproducing until about their tenth year and from then pairs will produce no more than one chick every two years. They live up to about 40 years. At the Auckland Islands the Gibson's albatrosses nest mainly along the tussocky tops of Adams Island. A small number, 50 to 100, nest at the southern end of Auckland Island and at Disappointment Island. Their low number on the main island is possibly due to disturbance and predation of eggs and chicks by wild pigs, although it could also be because the species has consistently favoured Adams Island for nesting.

Gibson's albatross is named after an Australian, Doug Gibson, who led a group of people who began a study of albatrosses, including the Auckland Islands ones, feeding off the coast of New South Wales in the 1950s. He developed a wandering albatross age assessment system based on plumage whiteness and known as the Gibson Plumage Index. Wandering albatrosses get whiter with age. An Adams Island bird banded by Doug Gibson in 1964 was still breeding in 2003.

Together, the Gibson's and Antipodean species make up about 50 percent of the world population of 'wandering' albatrosses. But their numbers have been steadily falling over the past few decades. The bycatch impact of longline fishing on these birds is being studied and addressed (see page 62).

The southern royal albatross appears not to be as badly hit by longline fishing. Although most of the population live at Campbell Island, Enderby and Adams Islands support small colonies. At Enderby Island (about 50 pairs), the nesting birds are easily spotted in the flat moor-like summit crest, sitting head and shoulders above the low

Extinct merganser

A LONG-BILLED MEMBER of the duck family, the Auckland Island merganser, has not been seen since 1902, when two were shot. First collected in 1840 by a French expedition, it has only ever been seen at Auckland and Adams Islands. It apparently inhabited freshwater creeks as well as sheltered inshore areas, feeding on fish, crabs and other crustaceans, molluscs and marine worms.

Cape pigeons feed on swarms of krill off Davis Island in Port Ross. TUI DE ROY

vegetation. White-capped albatrosses nest mainly on Disappointment Island, where there are an estimated 65,000 pairs.

A fourth albatross, the circumpolar light-mantled sooty albatross, is represented at the Auckland Islands by about 5,000 pairs.

Smaller seabirds breeding at the Auckland Islands include white-fronted tern, Antarctic prion, fulmar prion, white-chinned petrel, white-headed petrel, subantarctic diving petrel, white-faced storm petrel, black-bellied storm petrel, grey-backed storm petrel, northern giant petrel and Snares cape pigeon. A few giant petrels nest near the Sandy Bay sea lion colony, where they scavenge for afterbirth and dead pups during the breeding season.

Of the three penguin species recorded breeding at the Auckland Islands, only the yellow-eyed penguin *Megadyptes antipodes* is conspicuous. The population, estimated at over 500 pairs, is based at Enderby Island and other islands in the Port Ross area. Eastern rockhopper and erect-crested penguins are in low numbers.

Another prominent seabird at Enderby Island is the Auckland Island shag *Leucocarbo colensoi*, which nests in colonies at the cliff edges. The population is estimated to be less than 1,000 pairs.

There are more endemic land birds at the Auckland Islands than at other groups. The list runs to six: a rail, snipe, teal, banded dotterel, tomtit and pipit. The Auckland Island rail *Rallus pectoralis muelleri* was 'rediscovered' in 1989 on Adams Island. It also occurs at Disappointment Island. Probably the rarest of the Auckland Island endemic land birds is the banded dotterel *Charadrius bicinctus exilis*, which can be seen patrolling the coastline on Enderby Island. The snipe and teal are on most of the islands except the main Auckland Island, where pigs and cats have probably put paid to them. The teal are most often seen feeding in the bull kelp and amongst stranded seaweed in sheltered spots.

A race of New Zealand falcon inhabits the Auckland Islands, the only raptor in the New Zealand subantarctic region. It can be seen chasing smaller birds through the coastal forest. Two mainland parakeet species – red-crowned and yellow-crowned – have established populations at the Auckland Islands.

Of the 70 birds observed at the Auckland Islands, at least 46 are breeding.

Yellow-eyed penguins on coastal turf at Enderby Island. CHRIS CARROLL

The Auckland Island rail is found only on predator-free islands in the Auckland Islands group. ROD MORRIS

Bird of prey: the New Zealand falcon is established at the Auckland Islands – the only raptor of the New Zealand subantarctic islands. TUI DE ROY

The terrestrial invertebrate communities at the Auckland Islands are extensive. Some 180 insect species have been recorded, with about a third of them being endemic to the group. An endemic genus of stoner, *Aucklandobius*, has four species, three of which are flightless. Twelve of 45 moths recorded here are endemic. They include the sod webworm moth and several sedge or grass-leaf miners. The large weevil *Oclandius laeviusculus* is abundant on Adams Island, where there are no mice to feed on it.

Alien mammals at the Auckland Islands comprise pigs, cats and mice on Auckland Island, and cats and mice on Masked Island in Carnley Harbour.

A red-crowned parakeet feeds on bidibid seeds at Enderby Island. TUI DE ROY

SEASON OF DEATH

IN A MATTER OF WEEKS in January-February 1998, the sea lion population at the Auckland Islands suffered an epidemic that wiped out 60 percent of that season's pups (1,606) and at least 74 adults. It was a calamity for a species already on the threatened list, and it demonstrated that the New Zealand sea lion, with most breeding concentrated at one island group, is highly vulnerable to disease and problems in the food supply.

Researchers undertaking population studies at Enderby and Dundas Islands discovered the widespread deaths. Pups died underweight and many of the adults had swellings and lesions around the throat. Urgent efforts were made to identify the cause. A helicopter was despatched to collect tissue samples that were analysed at laboratories at Palmerston North (Massey University), Auckland, Lower Hutt, Rotterdam and New York. The cause of death in most animals was from bacterial infection. Tests at Massey University implicated the organism *Campylobacter*. It is possible that this organism occurs normally in the sea lions, but environmental conditions in 1998 may have stressed large numbers of them, lowering their immunity.

Further problems were identified in 2002 and 2003. Pup numbers were lower than normal (5 to 15 percent mortality rate for pups up to two months). Pup weights, which have declined since the 1980s, were also the lowest ever recorded. The weights reflect the health of the mothers, whose milk-fat levels are the lowest reported for any member of the seal family. Declines in maternal condition, milk-fat percentages and pup weight are probably a consequence of limitations in the food supply.

A bull sea lion surveys the beach at Sandy Bay, Enderby Island, at the height of the breeding season. Rival beachmaster bulls have staked out the beach and gathered females around them. A number of new-born pups are slumped on the sand. TUI DE ROY

Protection extends seawards

BLANKET PROTECTION FOR ALL LIFE out to 12 nautical miles – that is the promise of the New Zealand subantarctic region's first marine reserve, declared in January 2003. At 484,000 ha, the Auckland Islands Marine Reserve is the second largest in New Zealand after the subtropical Kermadec Islands Marine Reserve.

The Auckland Islands reserve builds on protection for inshore waters provided by a marine mammal sanctuary that was declared in 1993 to help keep the sea lions safe. Under the rules for the marine reserve, no fish or other species can be taken by commercial or recreational fishers between the shoreline and the territorial limit. That includes all harbours and inlets.

An area of continental shelf inside the reserve is an important nursery for southern blue whiting and arrow squid. Inshore, the commonest fish are in the nototheniid cod group. In the 1990s, a scampi fishery was found near the Auckland Islands.

The kelp forests along the eastern shores are especially impressive. A new species of large kelp in the genus *Lessonia* combines with the cosmopolitan bladder kelp *Macrocystis pyrifera* to dominate the sublittoral zone.

The giant Auckland Island spider crab *Jacquinotia edwardsii* is abundant. Among the krill species found near the Auckland Islands, *Munida gregaria* is common.

A lonely wind-swept corner: North West Cape, Auckland Island.
ANDRIS APSE

CAMPBELL ISLAND / MOTU IHUPUKU

New Zealand's southernmost subantarctic territory, the Campbell Island group lies 660 km south of Bluff, near the southern margin of the Campbell Plateau. Like the other two volcanic groups, Auckland and Antipodes Islands, it comprises a large main island, Campbell Island (11,268 ha) and several satellite islands, of which Dent (23 ha) and Jacquemart (19 ha) are the largest. The highest point is Mt Honey (569 m) on the south side of Perseverance Harbour. As at the Auckland Islands, the eastern side of the main island is heavily indented by fiord-like bays and inlets, the longest being Perseverance Harbour. High cliffs line much of the western side.

Campbell Island and its satellites are the eroded remains of a shield volcano of Miocene age, 6–11 million years old, embedded in continental crust. The volcanism was probably centred on the Dent Island-Northwest Bay area. Sea erosion has dismantled the western side of the volcano. The ancient Palaeozoic basement rock is composed of mica schist at least 450 million years old,

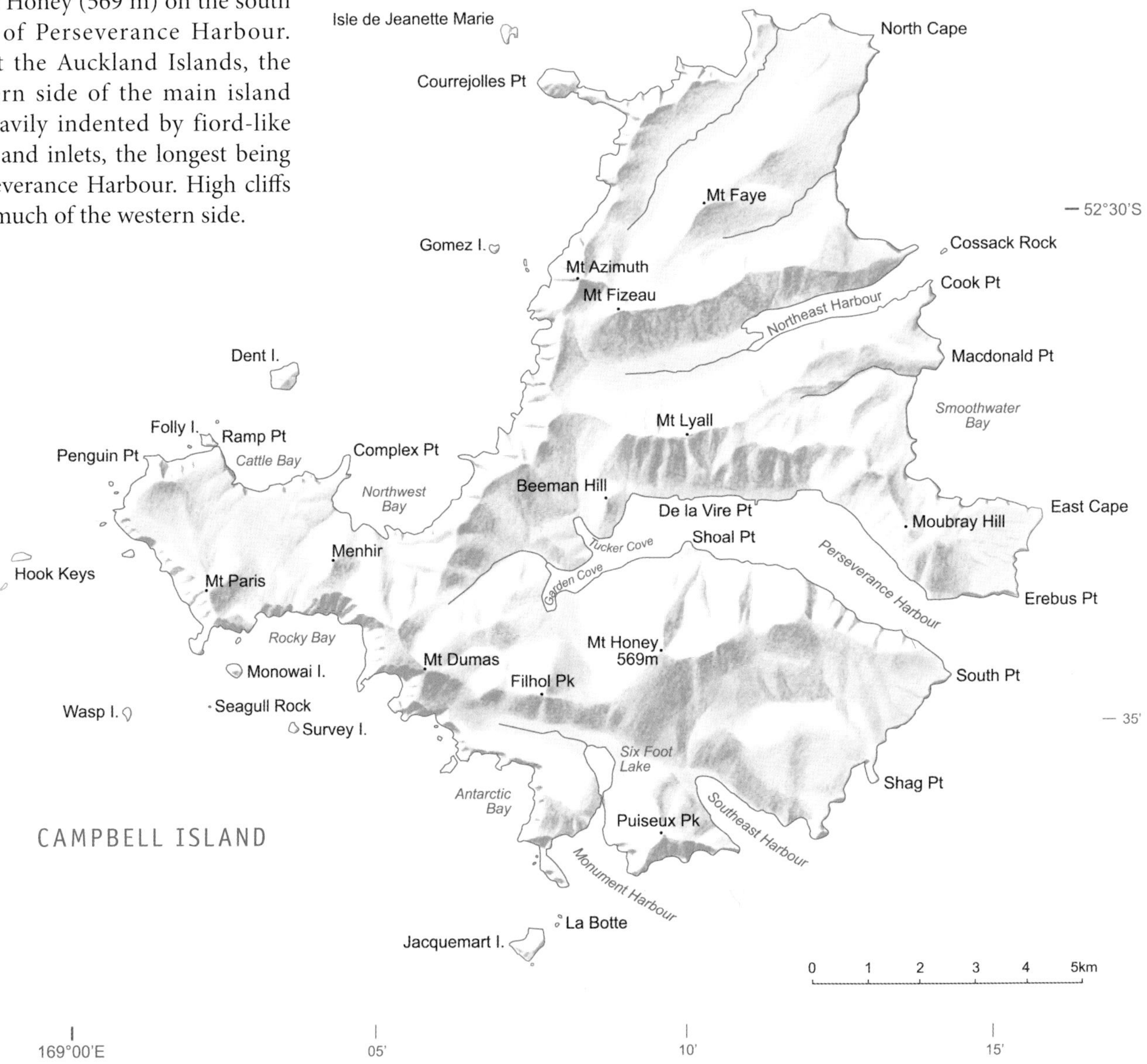

some of which is exposed at Complex Point, Northwest Bay. Overlying the schist is a younger (Cretaceous–Cenozoic) sequence of sandstone, mudstone, conglomerate and white cherty limestone, which forms spectacular cliffs above Northwest Bay.

During the ice ages of the last two million years, glaciers formed on the main island, leaving landforms such as U-shaped valleys, cirques and moraines. Post-glacial peat deposits mantle much of the land.

Rocks, plants and seabirds: the essence of Campbell Island. This rock wall is a dyke, formed naturally from an intrusion of igneous rock during the island's volcanic history. The yellow flowerheads are of the megaherb *Bulbinella rossii*. Gliding across the scene is a southern royal albatross. CHRIS CARROLL

Below: Dent Island, off the west coast of Campbell Island, is a steep-sided refuge for Campbell Island teal. In the foreground is the channel between Folly Island at left and Ramp Point on the main island. BRIAN RANCE

Rain and rainbows are commonplace at Campbell Island. CHRIS CARROLL

West of Campbell Island and the Campbell Plateau is a deep oceanic trench, on the other side of which is Macquarie Island, 700 km southwest of Campbell.

Located midway between the Antarctic and Subtropical Convergences, the Campbell Island group has the coolest (mean annual temperature, 6°C) and probably cloudiest climate in the New Zealand subantarctic region. A permanent weather station on Campbell provides comprehensive climate data. In an average year rain falls on 325 days (89 percent of the year), although mostly as drizzle or light showers. Light snowfalls are common in winter and spring. As at the other four groups, westerly winds prevail and here they reach hurricane force at times.

Campbell Island flora

Grassland covers much of the land, with the tussock-forming *Poa litorosa* and *Chionochloa antarctica* the dominant species. Both are regionally endemic. A rarer grass of shorter stature found in upland areas is *Poa aucklandica* var. *campbellensis*. The removal of sheep and cattle from the main island in recent years has led to a dramatic recovery in the vegetation, with the megaherbs as well as the grasses benefiting.

Megaherbs occur from sea level to the summit ridges. In places they form colourful meadows but they also grow interspersed with tussock grasses. All three daisy species of *Pleurophyllum* occur here: *P. speciosum*, *P. criniferum* and *P. hookerii*. *P. hookerii* is also found at the Auckland Islands and Macquarie Island. Two large carrot relatives, *Anisotome latifolia* and *A. antipoda*, are also prominent.

A colourful mat of seaweed decorates a sheltered shoreline at low tide, Campbell Island.
CHRIS CARROLL

Below: The spectacular flowers of the megaherb *Anisotome latifolia*, a giant member of the carrot family, catch the last sunshine of the day at Campbell Island. Dent Island is in the background.
CHRIS CARROLL

Macquarie Island cabbage *Stilbocarpa polaris* has survived the browsing by sheep and cattle. Less palatable to sheep, the lily *Bulbinella rossii*, largest member of its genus, forms extensive meadows on the main island.

Above an altitude of about 300 m, the herbs *Bulbinella rossii* and *Pleurophyllum hookerii* and the rush *Marsippospermum gracile* are prominent on the peat moor. Also found in the uplands are two endemic blue-flowered forget-me-nots, *Myosotis antarctica* and *M. capitata*, neither of which is common. A gentian *Gentiana antarctica*, endemic to Campbell Island, produces flowers that vary in colour between purple-blue and deep pink. Another significant herb is the rosette daisy *Damnamenia vernicosa*, which is endemic to the Campbell and Auckland Island groups.

The resurgence of plant life on the main island following grazing is well demonstrated by a species of cress, *Cardamine*, which grows much larger than previously recorded. During the sheep and cattle era it managed to survive at rocky bluff refuges.

A shrubland zone ranges from the shoreline to about 180 metres above sea level. The tallest species are the grass tree *Dracophyllum longifolium* and its close relative *D. scoparium*, which form a dwarf forest three to five metres tall and in places too dense to walk through. Shrubs of *Coprosma* and *Myrsine* are also present.

In gullies and in the shrubland, two ferns are common: prickly shield fern *Polystichum vestitum* and water fern *Histiopteris incisa*. There are mosses everywhere, with 119 species recorded.

As a result of introductions mainly during the farming era Campbell Island has the largest number of alien plant species of any of the New Zealand subantarctic groups – a total of 81.

The only true tree on the island is a single sitka spruce planted as a memorial at Camp Cove at the head of Perseverance Harbour in the early 1900s.

Campbell Island fauna

A world centre for albatross diversity, the Campbell Islands group hosts more species than any other subantarctic group except Crozet in the southern Indian Ocean. At Campbell six albatross species are breeding (compared to Crozet's seven), and one of the six breeds nowhere else. This is the Campbell mollymawk *Thalassarche impavida*, whose population is estimated at 26,000 pairs. They nest in northern parts of the main island, either in colonies of their own or mixed with the grey-headed mollymawk *T. chrysostoma*, which is circumpolar. The Campbell mollymawk is distinguished from the similar-looking black-browed mollymawk *T. melanophrys* (another circumpolar species, breeding here in low numbers) by a honey-coloured iris, a bolder black eyebrow and a bill of slightly different colour and shape. Two great albatrosses nest at Campbell: the southern royal

Endemic albatross: this colony of Campbell mollymawks, with chicks occupying the nests, stretches along the cliffs at North Cape, Campbell Island. TUI DE ROY

A light-mantled sooty albatross chick is fed by its parent at Monument Harbour, Campbell Island. TUI DE ROY

After the storm, Southern Royal Albatross with fledgling, Campbell Island.
MIKE DELLAMORE, *R.V. TIAMA*

albatross *Diomedea epomophora* and, in very low numbers, Antipodean albatross *Diomedea antipodensis*. Campbell Island is the southern royal's main breeding ground. The population is estimated at 14,000 pairs but because of a biennial breeding pattern, only about half the population is nesting in any one year. The sixth species is the circumpolar light-mantled sooty albatross *Phoebetria palpebrata*, which typically nests on cliff ledges and other steep places.

Campbell Island is also the main breeding ground for the yellow-eyed penguin *Megadyptes antipodes*, a New Zealand endemic and one of the world's rarest penguins. A population of 2,000 individuals – 500 to 600 breeding pairs – is estimated. More timid than other species, they form loose colonies in coastal vegetation. The eastern rockhopper penguin *Eudyptes chrysocome filholi* also breeds here but is in trouble. In the 40 years to 1985, the rockhopper population fell dramatically – and is probably continuing to fall (see page 74). Occasional visits have been recorded for three Antarctic penguin species – gentoo, chinstrap and Macaroni – and two species, king and royal, which have strongholds at Macquarie Island.

Among the other seabirds breeding at the Campbell Island group, members of the petrel family are prominent.

A yellow-eyed penguin, Campbell Island.
TUI DE ROY

The small, predator-free islands are home to large numbers of white-chinned petrel as well as sooty shearwater. Northern giant petrel, subantarctic diving petrel and grey-backed storm petrel also breed here. In addition, the New Zealand antarctic tern *Sterna vittata bethunei*, has its main breeding ground here. It is a rare subspecies, restricted to the New Zealand subantarctic islands and Stewart Island/ Rakiura. Brown skua also nest at Campbell Island.

Endemic to the group, the Campbell Island shag *Leucocarbo campbelli* nests at cliff-edge colonies. It feeds in sheltered waters, often in rafts of up to 100 birds, along the eastern side of the main island. The population is estimated at 1,000.

All birds nesting on the main island have benefited from the removal of farm animals, the subsequent disappearance of feral cats and the recent eradication of rats (see page 67). In the future, the main island may be repopulated with endemic land birds that have survived only on the small predator-free islands – and the smaller petrels will be able to re-establish.

Three land birds occur here: a teal, snipe and New Zealand pipit. The snipe was discovered in 1997 on Jacquemart Island (see opposite page). The flightless Campbell Island teal *Anas nesiotis*, one of the world's rarest ducks, was rediscovered on Dent Island, off Northwest Bay, in 1975. In recent years the species has been reintroduced on to Campbell Island, thanks to a Mainland New Zealand breeding programme and rat eradication (see page 67).

A total of 29 birds breed at Campbell Island, with 42 others recorded.

Among the marine mammals, seals are well represented at Campbell Island. There are populations of New Zealand sea lion, New Zealand fur seal and southern elephant seal, although breeding is relatively limited. The Northwest Bay beach is a haven for sea lions and elephant seals, which haul out on the sand. The elephant seals inhabit mud wallows near the shoreline; the sea lions often explore further inland, penetrating the dense shrublands. Sea lion breeding has increased. In 2003, 350 pups were counted at Campbell Island. Southern right whales gather in winter at Northwest Bay and other sites close to the main island, although not in the numbers seen at the Auckland Islands.

A pair of brown skua with chick, Campbell Island. GRAEME TAYLOR

Newly released: These New Zealand-bred Campbell Island teal are fitted with transmitters connected to small aerials. ANDRIS APSE

The invertebrate fauna at Campbell Island is reasonably well studied. Some 275 insects have been described, 40 percent of them endemic. The Campbell Island weta *Notoplectron campbellensis* is found now only on a few small, rat-free islands but the large weevil *Oclandius cinereus* survives in fields of *Bulbinella rossii* on the main island. Among the 29 moths, *Campbellana attenuata* is possibly the world's only flightless carposinid. A sod webworm moth, abundant only on Dent Island, has legs modified for jumping to compensate for reduced wings. Nine of the moths are endemic. The eradication of rats on Campbell Island will enable some of the large-bodied invertebrates to recolonise the main island.

The only freshwater fish on Campbell Island is a galaxiid common on mainland New Zealand and Australia and also at the Auckland Islands. Koaro *Galaxias brevipinnis* is a scaleless fish that grows to 200 mm in freshwater. It prefers quick-flowing streams.

A Sensational Discovery

IN NOVEMBER 1997, Department of Conservation staff searching for teal on 19 ha Jacquemart Island off the south coast of Campbell Island discovered a new kind of subantarctic land bird: Campbell Island snipe.

The first bird was flushed out of tussock grasses by a dog especially trained for bird-tracking. By the time the rangers and their three dogs were flown off the island by helicopter three hours later they had encountered a total of 10 snipe. The population on this small island could be as high as 60.

The party had to search in rough weather, with snow squalls and winds of up to 40 knots lashing the island. They found no teal.

Fitting neatly into a ranger's hand, the new snipe weighs as little as 80 g. It has an unusually long bill and mottled-brown plumage similar to that of its three cousins to the north, the snipe of Auckland, Snares and Antipodes Islands. These birds fly but only when they have to, and not very far.

The chance discovery caused great excitement among ornithologists. This snipe is the first subspecies of any New Zealand bird discovered in the past 100 years.

Presumably it lived on the main island before about 1810, when rats were introduced. Cats came later and no doubt finished off any snipe remaining on Campbell Island. Jacquemart Island, 1 km from the coast, is the southernmost island of the group.

A bird in the hand: Campbell Island snipe, discovered on Jacquemart Island in 1997. DEPARTMENT OF CONSERVATION

Not since 1897, when the Stewart Island subspecies of snipe was found, has there been a discovery at subspecies level in the New Zealand region. The Stewart Island snipe died out in the 1960s when rats invaded its last refuge on Big South Cape Island.

Snipe are related to a group of wading birds, including godwits, curlews and sandpipers, but instead of inhabiting estuaries and inlets they live in tussock grassland, shrubland and forest.

The Jacquemart Island discovery increased the number of endemic land birds inhabiting the New Zealand subantarctic islands from 14 to 15.

Jacquemart Island, where the Campbell Island snipe was discovered in 1997. TUI DE ROY

Macquarie Island Links

SOUTHWEST of Campbell Island, at 54 degrees south, Macquarie Island is a relatively young island with tangible links to the New Zealand groups.

It was forced up from the ocean floor about 700,000 years ago by the collision of the Australian and Pacific Plates – the only place on earth where mid-ocean crustal rocks are exposed at the surface. The collision squeezed out an elongated island 34 km in length by up to 5 km wide.

An Australian territory, Macquarie shares a number of plants as well as several seabird and marine mammal species with the New Zealand islands. With a mean annual temperature of 4.4°C, Macquarie has no woody plants among its 41 native species. Its best-known plant is *Stilbocarpa polaris*, the Macquarie Island cabbage, which was eaten by sealers to prevent scurvy.

Sprawling penguin colonies and large numbers of elephant seals are among the island's wildlife features. Before the island was declared a wildlife sanctuary in 1933, seals and penguins were slaughtered for their fur and oil. Australian Antarctic explorer Douglas Mawson described the island as 'one of the wonder spots of the world'.

Macquarie Island is a Tasmanian State reserve managed by the Tasmanian Parks and Wildlife Service. The scientific programme is administered by the Australian Antarctic Division based in Tasmania. Macquarie was listed as a World Heritage Area in 1997, mainly because of its unique geological history. A marine reserve surrounds the island.

With eyes made for deep diving, a young elephant seal rests on the shore at Campbell Island. CHRIS CARROLL

3

A Conservation Heartland

NEW ZEALAND'S SUBANTARCTIC ISLANDS rank among the toughest places in the world for conservation work. Consider the remote mid-ocean setting, a forbidding climate and a fragile environment that is also physically testing, then throw into the mix a world-significant array of biota, much of it rare and endemic, and some critically endangered. All of which adds up to a conservation challenge and a half.

Every year scientific and management expeditions set out for the region to work with special elements of the flora and fauna or to maintain facilities and historic sites.

Official policy aims to restore, where necessary, ecosystems and biota that maintain the ecological integrity and biodiversity of the islands. Chief among the management techniques relied on to deliver such an objective are the eradication of pest animals and plants, and the reintroduction of species lost to an ecosystem in the past.

At Campbell Island, the snipe and teal recovery stories, triggered by the stunning success of rat eradication (page 67), are twin triumphs of a rare kind.

The discovery of the Campbell Island snipe on sheer-sided Jacquemart Island in 1997, was exciting in itself; but the little bird's subsequent self-transfer to the main island, newly rid of rats, across one kilometre of water, was an astonishing achievement, especially as snipe are rather reluctant fliers.

It is assumed that for decades the snipe on Jacquemart, no bigger than a blackbird, have periodically flown over to the main island only to be killed by rats or cats on arrival – certainly before any human visitors there could record them.

But they are trying hard now to become less endangered. In May 2003, an expedition looking for sign of rats happened upon snipe-like footprints at Six Foot Lake, near coastline adjacent to Jacquemart Island. Then in March 2005, two birds were seen near the same lake and one was caught – proof positive of the homecoming. Even more exciting, the bird in hand was a fully-feathered chick. Snipe had not only come home to roost – they were breeding.

In February 2006 a survey team reported 31 snipe sightings. Seventeen birds, including five chicks, were caught for measuring and released. A formal scientific description and naming process was initiated – the first new bird to be named in New Zealand in over 100 years.

Campbell Island teal have also made a spectacular return to the main island. In September 2004, 50 teal bred in captivity on mainland New Zealand went 'home'. The release stirred international interest.

The story began in the 1970s, when they were rediscovered on Dent Island – the world's rarest ducks. In 1984 and 1990, a total of 11 teal were brought to New Zealand to lessen the risk of extinction. Not until 1994 was there any breeding.

The birds reintroduced in 2004 came from Mt Bruce National Wildlife Centre and predator-free Whenua Hou/ Codfish Island, off Stewart Island. In September 2005, after rigorous testing for diseases, another 55 teal were released at three different areas of Campbell Island – Perseverance Harbour, Northwest Bay and Six Foot Lake.

In 2006, came strong evidence the teal were breeding on the main island: an expedition located ducklings, juveniles and unbanded birds in good number. DOC is close to achieving its goal for the species, which is to re-establish teal on the main island so that further intensive management is no longer necessary.

The teal and snipe stories both deserved to be headline news. They also reinforced the New Zealand subantarctic region's reputation as a conservation heartland where major gains are possible.

In recent years, improving technology and management techniques have allowed a more proactive approach to conservation, although in a fragile environment like the subantarctic islands, every possible impact has to be weighed up against the benefits for the ecosystems and the species involved. Protocols continue to be written about the care that needs to be taken.

One species with a long hands-on history, Campbell Island's southern royal albatross, has been the subject of remedial action lately. More than 35,000 birds were banded between the early 1940s and late 1990s. A combination of weak metal and poor banding technique resulted in leg injury – or potential injury – to about one in ten of these birds. That problem is being overcome by teams of conservation staff who are rebanding some of the albatrosses to maintain a marked population and removing all other bands. In the process they are learning things – for example, the survival pattern of these birds, since many birds have not been seen since they were banded. To date, a bird aged 38 years holds the longevity record. The population probably greatly suffered during the farming era but recovered to about 8,000 nests annually by the 1990s.

Rat eradication on Campbell Island has been a turning point for that island's ecology. Seabirds driven away by the rats – and cats in earlier years – are making a comeback. They include the delicate grey-backed storm petrel, which is nesting again. A land bird, the New Zealand pipit, which was only occasionally recorded on the main island, is also recolonising the main island after being confined to the islets for more than a century.

As Campbell Island recovers something of its pre-human ecology, the conservation focus is switching to the Auckland Islands, where there lies a challenge greater than the Campbell Island rats – feral pigs. Surprisingly, given the contact ships have had with the Auckland Islands in the past, rats have never established on the main island.

Pigs have run wild on the main Auckland Island since Bristow's discovery of the group 200 years ago. They have caused severe damage to the island's ecology, ranging from rooting out megaherbs on the summit crest to eating the

Predator: this feral pig has just finished devouring a white-capped albatross chick at its nest near South West Cape, Auckland Island. The photographer was too late to save the chick. TUI DE ROY

chicks and eggs of threatened ground-nesting birds and destroying their nests. In combination with the cats, pigs are thought to have eliminated Auckland Island merganser, teal, rail and snipe as well as smaller burrow-nesting petrels from the main island. They continue to wreak havoc on albatross colonies and the natural vegetation.

Conservation managers are gearing up for a major assault on the pigs after long thinking that little could be done. The pigs roam everywhere on the main island, even into the intertidal zone where they browse on seaweed.

An eradication programme targeting the pigs – and cats as well – is envisaged. It will cost several million dollars and span several years. To succeed, it will have to cover an area five times the size of Campbell Island. In anticipation of an eradication project, some pigs have already been captured live and transferred to mainland New Zealand as examples of a 'rare breed'.

There can be no middle measures of control. Eradication is the goal – and Campbell Island the inspiration for it.

Trials on poison type and bait laying are in the wind. Satellite tracking of pigs fitted with transmitters should inform managers of the project about where they commonly travel. For example, are the mountain tops and ridge line and coastal margins the main target areas? A strategy that kills cats at the same time is the aim. Hunters on foot with dogs are probably not an option because of the cost, the ability of pigs to hide in dense vegetation and the risk both of dogs running wild and pigs being chased into the sea and swimming to smaller inshore islands.

Project planners have to consider the risk of a poison pellet programme to non-target species such as the scavenging skua and giant petrels, and the endemic falcon.

If sufficient funds and resources can be applied, the project stands a good chance of success. It would pave the way for restoration of the ecology of the largest New Zealand subantarctic island – a conservation goal of international importance.

In the mid-1990s, a Conservation Management Strategy (CMS) was developed for the New Zealand Subantarctic Islands. It has a 10-year vision, 1998-2008. Replacing the five management plans written in an earlier era, it speaks of 'integrated management' and a 'holistic approach'. The CMS management goals seek to preserve the island nature reserves in their natural state as far as possible and to achieve restoration where there has been damage or modification.

All islands have been ranked. There are only two categories – minimum impact and refuge. Most of the islands are in the former category, which is more protective. Entry is strictly limited. The refuge islands, less restrictive on visitors, include Auckland and Enderby Islands in the Auckland group, and Campbell Island. The distinction is based mainly on the degree of modification, whether introduced animals are or were present and whether they have had a significant impact on the flora and fauna, as in case of the refuge islands.

Impacts by visitors, including tourists, scientists and management personnel, are a particular focus for the CMS. Rules and limits on tourism in the region have been set by the CMS (see Chapter 6) and visitor impact monitoring, involving video and still-camera photography, has been established at key visitor sites in response to increasing tourism pressure. This monitoring will inform management decisions about the ongoing use of the islands.

The CMS promises real progress in conserving the rare and special elements of the region. Thirty-one birds are listed as threatened. The New Zealand sea lion is the priority marine mammal. Among a dozen plant species, two megaherbs endemic to The Snares are listed – the carrot relative *Anisotome acutifolia* and the large-leaved *Stilbocarpa robusta*. The threats to the plant life in the subantarctic are minor compared to the problems facing the fauna. Recovery plans, reviewable after five years, set out proactive measures aimed at increasing populations and reducing vulnerability.

The story of the Campbell Island snipe shows that significant discoveries can still occur in this region, and that the conservation goalposts are liable to move, requiring flexibility when it comes to deploying limited conservation resources.

Tracking teal at Six Foot Lake on Campbell Island with the help of a trained tracker dog. TIM SHAW

High seas: a westerly gale in the Southern Ocean produces large waves, where albatrosses and other seabirds make a living.
KIM WESTERSKOV

OCEAN FOCUS

A NEW FRONTIER FOR CONSERVATION is the ocean. In the New Zealand subantarctic zone, until recent times, the focus was on the five island groups and their terrestrial flora and fauna. Increasingly, however, the sea's complex and enigmatic ecosystems are seen as an important area for conservation work.

The Subantarctic Islands Conservation Management Strategy (1998–2008) emphasises the connection between seabirds and marine mammals breeding on land and a healthy marine ecosystem. The strategy also seeks the protection of the marine environment in the interests of conserving species at risk from fishing and other activities. It calls for more study of ocean biological processes and the impacts of human activities on these processes.

Since the strategy was published, the New Zealand Government has stated its interest in conserving marine biodiversity. It is committed to protecting a full range of natural marine habitats and ecosystems.

In 2003, NIWA scientist John Booth undertook a review of how much was known about the marine environment to the south of mainland New Zealand, given that the region's remote, vast and deep-water nature had stood in the way of a thorough understanding of it.

Based on what was then known and published about New Zealand's subantarctic marine environment, he concluded that the region had 'relatively low levels of phytoplankton biomass and low levels of primary production' despite its importance for seabirds, seals and fish (phytoplankton anchors the ocean food webs). Primary production is 'iron-limited' as a result of low levels of dissolved iron.

In terms of the pelagic life, the studies reviewed by Dr Booth suggest it resembles communities in the seas around the New Zealand mainland – 'little stands out as being particularly unique'. Seamounts within the region host the most diverse and productive assemblages, with 190 of fish species recorded by research and commercial fishing catch records.

Inshore communities around the island groups, however, contain 'significant local and southern New Zealand endemism'. Each group has assemblages of seaweeds, invertebrates and fish that are found only there. Not surprisingly perhaps, the Auckland Islands group, because of its size and range of

A New Zealand fisheries inspection team returns to the frigate *HMNZS Canterbury* after boarding a foreign fishing vessel in the New Zealand subantarctic region. BARRY HARCOURT

habitats, has the most diverse marine life.

Average sea temperatures have increased by 0.5°C since the 1950s, with human-induced global warming possibly implicated.

Much of the sea floor across the Southern Plateau (which covers 433,600 sq km, extends 1,100 km south of the South Island and incorporates the Campbell and Bounty Plateaus and Pukaki Rise) comprises soft sediment, predominantly a 'calcareous ooze'.

Dr Booth, in his report to the Department of Conservation, recommended that protection be extended across the territorial seas around the island groups. A marine reserve already exists at the Auckland Islands (see page 49).

In January 2006, the Government released a Marine Protected Areas Policy for New Zealand, including the subantarctic region. The policy, developed by the Department of Conservation and the Ministry of Fisheries, calls for the creation of a representative network of marine protected areas.

Soon afterwards, the Ministry of Fisheries, with the agreement of the commercial fishing industry, announced a significant conservation measure – the closure of areas of the subantarctic zone to bottom trawling and dredging. Although the proposal applied to the New Zealand Exclusive Economic Zone as a whole, some of the largest areas designated for closure were in the subantarctic. They comprised two large areas west and east of Campbell Island and another large area south of the Antipodes group, plus two smaller areas surrounding the Campbell and Bounty Islands groups.

Together, these areas comprise about a quarter of the New Zealand subantarctic zone. Bottom trawling can cause severe damage to the seabed and therefore to benthic biodiversity. Its exclusion from large areas of the subantarctic is a welcome concession from the fishing industry, although there could be debate about the location of the closure areas and how much trawling is allowed in seamounts outside the closed areas.

Conservation work these days does not stop at the 12 nautical mile territorial limit. It extends a long way seawards. Of particular interest is the accidental killing of seabirds (see box, page 64), sea lions and fur seals by the deep-water fishing fleets.

Every year sea lions are drowned in nets, and when the number of deaths reaches a prescribed level (the limit was 150 in 2006), the squid fishery is closed by the New Zealand Government. Trawlers operating in the Auckland Islands area carry nets with sea lion exclusion devices (SLEDs) but so far the technology has had only marginal success.

Whales, in particular southern right whales, are protected not only by marine mammal protection zones created under New Zealand legislation but also by the Southern Ocean Whale Sanctuary, created by the International Whaling Commission in 1994. The sanctuary covers 11 million square miles south of latitude 40 degrees.

SEABIRDS AT RISK

TO ADDRESS THE INTERNATIONAL ISSUE of seabirds being killed by trawlers and long-line vessels, Southern Seabird Solutions was formed in 2002 to promote the conservation of seabirds throughout the Southern Ocean. It is an international alliance of government, fishing industry and environmental groups working to promote responsible fishing practices.

Large numbers of albatrosses and petrels have been killed in recent decades by fishing techniques, in particularly long-lining. Baited hooks set from the stern of long-line vessels attract many seabirds. An estimated 200 million hooks are set in Southern Hemisphere waters every year. An additional hazard comes from seabirds becoming entangled in trawling gear. Over half the albatross populations that are being monitored around the world are declining. For most of these species, fishing is the only known threat.

Thirty-five different species of albatross and petrel have been recorded caught in New Zealand fisheries since 1996. The most commonly caught species are white-capped albatross, white-chinned petrel and grey petrel.

Long-line and trawl vessels are being offered advice and education on bird-safe practices and equipment. In New Zealand, fishing companies are levied to pay, in part, for the collection of information on seabirds and the numbers being caught, and for research into ways of reducing bycatch levels. The levy also contributes to research on the impacts on the New Zealand sea lion from squid trawling on the Auckland Islands Shelf.

Lucky to survive: this southern royal albatross continued breeding on Campbell Island after its leg was impaled on a long-line hook. The hook was removed by scientists involved in the albatross debanding project. CHRISSY WICKES

Hands-on conservation work: Department of Conservation ranger Jeremy Carroll checks out a white-chinned petrel chick at Disappointment Island. TUI DE ROY

Albatross study

A study that aims to map the foraging pattern of white-capped albatrosses and where they interact with fishing fleets, began in 2006. The study is part of an ongoing assessment of the bycatch impact of fishing vessels, long-line fleets in particular, on seabirds.

A Niwa-led expedition camped on the main Auckland Island and attached a mixture of satellite tags, GPS units and geo-location loggers to selected birds. Eighteen geo-location loggers were fitted and these will be recovered in successive summers to create tracking maps for the individual birds.

Most of the 60–70,000 white-capped albatross live on Disappointment Island, off the west coast of Auckland Island, but a few thousand pairs nest elsewhere in the group.

During their month on Auckland Island the scientists noted the appalling impact of wild pigs on the white-capped and Gibson's albatrosses nest areas. There was daily evidence of pigs uprooting the white-cappeds' pedestal nests and eating chicks and eggs. The larger Gibson's albatrosses, which nest at ground level, were also attacked.

Conserving history

Protecting historic sites and features is an important part of the work of the Department of Conservation in the subantarctic islands.

The Conservation Management Strategy for the region sets priorities for historic resource conservation on the basis of themes and representative sites. Fifteen sites are actively managed for conservation. They span all the eras, including whaling, Maori occupation sites, shipwreck relics, early scientific visits, farming and the wartime Coastwatch operation.

The majority of recorded historic sites are in the Auckland Islands. A 2003 survey of the Auckland Islands, the most comprehensive of its kind yet undertaken, involved 15 specialists and documented 128 sites. Previously, there were 53 sites on the historic resources list. The additional sites included the remains of pastoral farming and Coastwatch jetties and emergency sheds. A castaway depot, erected by the New Zealand Government in the 1890s at Camp Cove, Carnley Harbour, was a site identified by the 2003 survey as being worthy of inclusion on the 'actively managed' list. Some superficial remains, probably representing the activities of the secretive sealers, were also discovered. These included old fireplaces and coppiced trees.

Excavation at the Sandy Bay early Polynesian occupation site during the 2003 Auckland Islands Heritage Inventory and Landscape project. PAUL DINGWALL/DEPARTMENT OF CONSERVATION

A similar intensive survey of the historic resources of Campbell Island is planned. The existing number of recorded historic sites (13) is likely to increase substantially. The Antipodes and Snares group have yet to be thoroughly surveyed for historical resources. At the rocky Bounty Islands there is little in the way of recorded historic features.

DOC historian Rachael Egerton says the subantarctic region poses special challenges for conserving historic resources. Most human activity there was of short duration, and the elements have taken their toll. 'It's amazing there's anything left given the environment – wet, windy and humid,' she says.

(See also Chapter 5)

KEEPING OUT INCURSIONS

STRINGENT EFFORTS are made to prevent potentially nasty things reaching the islands – rodents, foreign seeds and insects, and diseases. These efforts have high priority under the Subantarctic Islands Conservation Management Strategy, which recognises that it is wiser and more cost-effective to prevent incursions than have to deal with them once the foreign animal or plant has taken hold.

A 'quarantine' approach, backed up by education and rules, is required. Rules apply to everyone visiting the islands, including conservation staff, scientists, tourists and the media.

On tour ships, precautions are taken on board before any landings. All footwear and clothing must be clean. All vessels visiting the islands must have recent 'de-ratting' certificates and be free of exotic hull-encrusting organisms such as *Undaria* seaweed.

To some extent the nature of the subantarctic is protected by the 'moat' effect – the huge tracts of sea surrounding the islands. But it could take only one senseless act or omission for disaster to strike.

Removing the Pests

WHEN IT COMES TO CONSERVATION outcomes, restoring habitats and enhancing the survival of threatened species, nothing has been more important in recent years than the systematic removal of introduced animals.

Wherever the pest elimination work has succeeded, there has been a resurgence of bird life as well as native plant life such as the endemic megaherbs.

No mustelids were ever introduced to these islands. Stoats, ferrets and weasels, the scourge of mainland New Zealand native birds and reptiles, present no threat in the subantarctic. Another widespread pest on the mainland, brushtail possums from Australia, were also never introduced into the subantarctic. Nor were red deer, which mainland experience shows are capable of a devastating impact on native vegetation. Ship or black rats, even if they did get ashore at one time, never colonised the islands.

But other alien animals did make it. The list is long. There were liberations of pigs at the Auckland Islands from the early 1800s. Goats joined them – again, as a food resource for shipwreck victims. Goats were released at more islands than any other animal – Auckland, Enderby, Ewing, Ocean Islands in the Auckland group, as well as The Snares, Antipodes and Campbell groups. Sheep were also well spread. There were liberations at Auckland, Enderby, Rose and Adams Islands, Campbell and Antipodes. From 1850 through to the 1990s, cattle roamed around Enderby Island, first as castaway food and later as farm stock. There were also cattle at Rose, Campbell and Antipodes Islands. French Blue rabbits were released at Enderby and Auckland Islands in 1840 followed by mixed-breed rabbits at Rose Island ten years later. Brown (Norway) rats jumped ship at Campbell Island and mice invaded Auckland, Enderby and Antipodes Islands. Cats were released at Auckland and Campbell Islands, and they reached Masked Island in Carnley Harbour.

The impacts of these introductions were significant. Habitats were modified and some indigenous species were hit hard. A few species were saved from extinction only by their survival on small adjacent islands. By the 1980s, the presence of alien animals was accepted as inconsistent with the national nature reserve status of the islands.

The first moves to restore the balance were made against the Campbell Island sheep. Fences split the island into three blocks, and sheep were eliminated from them in turn – in 1970, 1984 and 1990–91. Some 1,200 were shot in November 1990 and the last stragglers the following year. Cattle had been removed in 1976. The removal of the sheep, and consequent recovery of the vegetation, had an unexpected spinoff: the cats disappeared, possibly because the vegetation reclaimed the grazed open areas and created a damp and closed habitat unsuitable for cats.

In 1987 the animal pest work took on a heightened resolve with the creation of the Department of Conservation. The Auckland Island goats were targeted. Fifty-eight goats were captured live and transferred to the New Zealand mainland as stock of possible genetic benefit to goat farming. Climate and habitat confined the goats to the Port Ross area. In 1989, hunters began a goat eradication programme and completed it within a couple of years.

Next in the firing line were Enderby's rabbits and cattle. Rabbit holes on the grass sward at Sandy Bay had trapped and killed many exploring sea lion pups, and the cattle had damaged and eaten out forest and herbfield. In the early 1990s, following the live capture of a number of rabbits and shorthorn cattle for the New Zealand Rare Breeds

Undaria threat

A LOOMING THREAT to inshore marine ecosystems in the subantarctic is the large brown Asian seaweed *Undaria pinnatifida*. Introduced accidentally into New Zealand in the 1980s, it has spread south as far as Paterson Inlet at Stewart Island/Rakiura, carried on the hulls of vessels, in ballast water or on mussel spat. Conservation staff are concerned this invasive seaweed will turn up sooner or later in the subantarctic islands. Tolerant of a wide range of habitats, it grows rapidly in depths up to 18 m and could displace indigenous seaweeds and change seabed communities.

Fishing, charter and recreational vessels visiting the New Zealand subantarctic islands commonly leave from ports that are infested with *Undaria*. A code of practice has been developed by the Ministry of Fisheries for the maritime industry and a public awareness programme aims to make vessel operators aware of the threat.

Conservation Society, the island was cleared of these animals. The mice also disappeared from Enderby Island – eradicated by the rabbit-poisoning programme.

Then came the eradication of Norway rats from Campbell Island. The previous New Zealand record for island rat eradication was held by the Kapiti Island project. Kapiti has a land area of 1,970 ha; Campbell Island is more than five times the size.

There are some major projects in the pipeline to complete the eradication of animal pests from the subantarctic islands, including the removal of pigs and cats from Auckland Island.

Campbell cleared of rats

CAMPBELL ISLAND is free of rats – free to become again a haven for subantarctic birds and other wildlife.

In May 2003, the Department of Conservation announced that an inspection team had spent four weeks on the island looking for evidence of rats and found none. Two years earlier, in July 2001, an ambitious rat-poisoning programme had been carried out at the island, involving 19 personnel and five helicopters. Brodifacoum bait was dropped across the main island and tiny Folly Island, with overlaps ensuring full coverage. Extra bait was laid across rocky cliffs.

A total of 120 tonnes of bait, in the form of cereal pellets, was bucket-spread by the helicopters. The cost of bait, sea transport, fuel, supplies, staff and helicopter time came to about $2 million.

After several years of planning it took just four weeks to complete the fieldwork, which was timed for July so as to cause the least disturbance to wildlife and to catch the rats at their hungriest time of year. Project leaders had been concerned that skuas might take the baits but no problem eventuated. Invertebrates, seabirds and seals appeared to be unaffected.

Conservation benefits are huge. More than 30 species are benefitting. They include the critically endangered teal and snipe, the endangered Campbell Island pipit, vulnerable species such as Campbell albatross, grey-headed albatross, grey petrel, yellow-eyed penguin and eastern rockhopper penguin, and endangered weevils, beetles, giant slug and other invertebrates. The plant communities will also benefit.

Campbell Island, the largest island in the world so far to be cleared of rats, formerly harboured a high density of brown or Norway rats *Rattus norvegicus*.

Another load of poison bait about to contribute to the eradication of rats on Campbell Island. PETE TYREE

The rat catchers: Campbell Island meteorological station on the shores of Perseverance Harbour was base camp for a massive rat-poisoning programme in july 2001. The scene here includes three of the five helicopters used in the operation and long rows of beige-coloured bait containers. PETE TYREE

Botanical art: *Myosotis capitata*, an endemic forget-me-not from Auckland and Campbell Islands, by artist Jo Ogier. She is among a select group of artists who have been assisted to visit the subantarctic islands in recent years. Courtesy of JO OGIER

Scientific Frontiers

'THIS PLACE I suppose abounds with seals,' whaler Abraham Bristow wrote of the Auckland Islands, which he put on European maps in August 1806. Noting the probability of 'a good harbour in the north end', he sailed by on the westerly conveyor belt, bound for Cape Horn out of Tasmania. Thus the first Europeans to lay eyes on the Auckland Islands had only resources in mind. Scientific exploration came decades later. In 1840, the British Antarctic Expedition led by James Clark Ross (later Sir James) called at the Auckland Islands with botanists Joseph Hooker and David Lyall, both aged 22, and two members of the expedition, Robert McCormick and John Robertson, who were seeking zoological and geological specimens. Hooker's contribution was outstanding, and he is remembered in the scientific names of several species, including one of the *Pleurophyllum* daisies and the sea lion, and Mt Hooker on Auckland Island. Lyall's name attaches to the *Olearia* tree daisy, first collected on this expedition, and Mt Lyall on Campbell Island.

Of interest is the preoccupation then with the plant life compared to the scientific emphasis today, which is mainly on birds, marine mammals and their ecosystems, and the threats they face. Hooker (later Sir Joseph) was entranced by the flora of the Auckland and Campbell groups. Some flowering plants were 'of peculiar interest ... more remarkable for their beauty and novelty than the flora of any other country can show'. At the Auckland and Campbell Islands he collected specimens of more than 100 flowering plants – an impressive record given the expedition's short stay – as well as some 200 species of seaweed, mosses, lichens and liverworts. Hooker's landmark publication, *Flora Antarctica*, includes numerous references to the New Zealand subantarctic islands. Dr McCormick, meanwhile, made the first collection of insects, and at the Auckland Islands he shot teal, merganser, bellbird and tui to show the western world.

The Ross expedition, with little understanding of ecological impacts, released enough animals to stock a farmyard: sheep, pigs, rabbits and hens. Vegetables and fruit trees were planted. The hens had laid eggs even before the expedition departed for Antarctica.

Scientist Paul Sagar measuring a Buller's mollymawk at The Snares as part of a long-term study of the species.
KENNEDY WARNE

When government steamers, from the late 1870s, began making calls at the islands to check for castaways, scientists were often aboard to make observations and collections. The naturalists included Sir James Hector, John Buchanan, Andreas Reischek, Thomas Kirk and Leonard Cockayne.

A multi-disciplinary stocktake of the nature of the Auckland Islands was undertaken in 1907 when the Canterbury Philosophical Institute's Auckland and Campbell Islands Expedition visited the group in the government steamship *Hinemoa*. Two years later the expedition members reported their findings in two volumes edited by Professor Charles Chilton.

Increasingly through the 20th century, scientific expeditions acknowledged the vulnerable nature of the sub-antarctic flora and fauna, and the research topics became more specialised. Since the early 1990s, scientific research has increased markedly. At the start of the 21st century about 50 permits a year were being issued. Collecting can range from bird lice to *Lepidoptera*, rock samples to rare plants. Research projects that shed light on at-risk species – and how to manage them – are favoured. Research has been conducted on sea lions and the rarer albatross species over many years.

Declining seabird numbers have thrown the spotlight on what is happening in the sea, and in this respect rockhopper penguin research is at the cutting edge (see page 74).

Another important study centres on the Gibson's wandering albatross *Diomedea gibsoni*, a species endemic to the Auckland Islands. The bulk of them breed on Adams Island.

Department of Conservation ranger Pete McClelland inspects a Gibson's wandering albatross nest on Adams Island. KATH WALKER

Prompted by concerns that the Gibson's albatross was being hard hit by longline fishing bycatch, a study of the bird was initiated in 1991. It involves a regular census and investigation of breeding success and population parameters. After seven years the research team, led by Kath Walker and Graeme Elliott, produced a reliable population estimate. The average annual number of pairs nesting on

A fishing fleet in subantarctic waters. KIM WESTERSKOV

Adams Island, where the bulk of the species is based, was 5,831 over the seven years – a decline from the 1973 estimate of 7,000 pairs, which the 1990s study says was probably on the low side. Increased mortality through bycatch in the longline fishery is considered to be the most likely cause of the decline.

The recent research has shed light on several aspects of the life and times of the Gibson's albatross. Breeding success among the Adams Island birds between 1991 and 1997 was calculated at 67 percent. Each pair attempts to raise a chick every second year but not all are successful. Nesting density has also been a focus of the research. A density of 3.2 nests per hectare has been calculated for the Adams Island study area. Compare this with an anecdotal report from 100 years earlier, when expedition members from the government steamship *Hinemoa* 'went up after albatross eggs … and we got two hundred eggs on about five acres.'

Of special interest, particularly in light of the fishery bycatch issue, is the foraging range of these birds. This information comes from tracking studies based on tiny transmitters that are fitted to selected birds and communicate their position via a satellite. It shows that both breeding and non-breeding Gibson's albatrosses routinely forage in the Tasman Sea off South Australia and Tasmania and occasionally to the east of the New Zealand mainland. One bird with a chick in the study area was located northeast of Sydney, 3,300 km from Adams Island, while on an 8–10 day foraging trip typical of breeding birds.

Although the Department of Conservation approves and oversees research work in the subantarctic islands and does some of the research itself, it does not resource all the research projects. University and Crown research institutes are active in the New Zealand subantarctic region, and the fishing industry's Conservation Services Levy contributes towards research that promotes a better understanding of the impacts of fishing on protected

Megaherb Mysteries

Fascinating to visitors, puzzling to botanists, the megaherbs of the New Zealand subantarctic region have yet to reveal, conclusively, the reasons for their large leaves and colourful floral displays. There are at least 10 taxa endemic to the region, and they occur in four genera: *Anisotome*, *Bulbinella*, *Pleurophyllum* and *Stilbocarpa*.

A few theories exist. The size of the foliage is thought to be an adaptive response to cloudy, humid conditions and cool temperatures. An increase in leaf temperature of up to 15°C has been recorded on the corrugated leaves of *Pleurophyllum speciosum* at Campbell Island. As for the floral colours, one theory suggests that bright or dark colours absorb more warmth from the diluted sunlight than would lighter colours, enabling fertilisation and seed development to proceed more quickly in the short summer season. The colours may also serve to attract pollinators.

It is not known whether these plants are relics of an ancient, more widespread flora that pre-dates the ice ages or whether they evolved at their isolated islands. Whatever the reasons for their existence, size and colour, the megaherbs are huge contributors to the character of these islands.

The megaherb *Pleurophyllum speciosum* at Col Ridge, Campbell Island. TUI DE ROY

species, principally seabirds and marine mammals.

To guide applicants who want to do research work in the region and to assist the Department's assessment of the proposals, a subantarctic islands research strategy has been developed by the Southland Conservancy. Four research themes are described: natural ecosystems (including ocean dynamics, food webs and foraging behaviour), effects of introduced biota, human impacts, and non-biological sciences (geology, climatology, oceanography, atmospheric research). As an indication of priorities and to help guide future research, the strategy lists several study topics under each theme.

The strategy also emphasises the sensitivity of the islands as a research arena. All projects have to comply with a minimum impact code and quarantine requirements.

Predictably, the focus to date has been on the conspicuous fauna but there could well be a shift in the future towards the less visible – for example, climate-change impacts, understanding pathogens in the subantarctic environment, and how micro-organisms contribute to the wellbeing of life.

A light-mantled sooty albatross pair with their chick, Monument Harbour, Campbell Island. TUI DE ROY

Birds 'reappear' from bones

THE DISCOVERY of sub-fossil bird remains at a site above Perseverance Harbour in 2004 gave an insight into birdlife at Campbell Island in former times.

The leg bone of a parakeet/kakariki was included in the find. There are no previous records of parakeet ever having lived at Campbell. Bones of a sooty shearwater/titi and diving petrel were also uncovered at the same site. The titi bone exhibited a notch that, according to palaeobiologist Dr Richard Holdaway, was probably made by a New Zealand falcon, a race of which lives on at the Auckland Islands. Again, this is the first evidence of falcon at Campbell.

Back in 1840, an exploring British expedition found no land birds at all on Campbell Island. Rats introduced by sealing or whaling vessels in the early 1800s seemingly eliminated them from the main island. Only remnant populations were left, hiding out on small islands with little room for expansion.

Southern royal albatrosses engage in ritual display on a meadow of *Bulbinella* that has just finished flowering. TUI DE ROY

Tracks of breeding (black) and migrating (coloured) sooty shearwaters originating from Whenua Hou/Codfish Island, New Zealand.
(Shaffer et al. 2006)

A MAJOR INTERNATIONAL STUDY is shedding new light on where New Zealand-based sooty shearwaters/titi feed during the breeding season and where they travel on their migrations into the North Pacific. In their millions, they breed at The Snares and islands around Stewart Island/Rakiura.

The study, involving New Zealand, American and French scientists, is mapping the foraging and migration paths of sooty shearwaters using electronic data loggers.

Weighing just 10 grams and fitted on a leg band, the loggers record ambient light levels, pressure, and environmental temperature for up to 2 years. The time of sunrise and sunset, derived from measures of light intensity by the tag, allow day length and local noon to be determined, and thus calculation of a bird's longitude and latitude at sea.

Measured changes in pressure reveal diving behaviour (depths of 60 metres are not unusual), and temperature measurements allow scientists to evaluate the environment where titi travel on their journeys.

In the 2005 summer, 33 breeding titi were equipped with data loggers at two breeding colonies (Whenua Hou/Codfish and Mana Islands). Twenty birds were recaptured at the same breeding burrows in spring/summer 2006 after nearly 10 months of travel. In addition to making several trips to Antarctic waters, each bird completed a round-trip migration to the North Pacific (see figure) that totalled more than 60,000 km. These incredible migrations are among the longest, if not the longest, in the animal kingdom.

Loggers were redeployed for another year to compare feeding behaviour and migrations paths across multiple years to help the scientists evaluate climatic changes and how these might influence ocean ecology.

What's ailing the Rockhoppers?

BETWEEN 1942 AND 1985, the rockhopper penguin population at Campbell Island declined by 94 percent from 1.6 million breeding pairs to just 103,000 pairs, and all indications suggest that the decline has continued since the mid-1980s. A similar decline is thought to have occurred in the rockhopper population at the Antipodes.

Scientists in the 1980s suggested that the movement of ocean water bodies and sea temperature fluctuations had sent the ocean food web within the feeding range of the penguins into a spin, either reducing the rockhoppers' food supply or forcing them to switch to prey less appetising and of lower food value.

Since then scientists from New Zealand's National Institute of Water and Atmospheric Research have been on the case, using stable isotope analysis and some old penguin feathers from museum collections to try to get to the bottom of it.

Analysing the ratios of stable isotopes of carbon and nitrogen in feather proteins, they began to piece together a picture of the penguins' diet over time and the productivity of the seas. The nitrogen stable isotope ratio gives clues as to where in the food chain the penguins are feeding, and the carbon isotope ratio gives information about productivity patterns in the ocean.

Thanks to 19th century penguin-skin collectors and the cooperation of New Zealand, American and Austrian museums, the study was able to examine isotopes as far back as the 1880s. So, have the diets of New Zealand rockhopper penguins changed? The simple answer, say NIWA scientists David Thompson and Paul Sagar is 'no'. They found no change in the nitrogen signature over time, which means the rockhoppers' diet, based on shrimp-like krill, has remained more or less the same. The carbon isotope analysis, however, gave a different result, suggesting a decline in ocean productivity starting in the late 1940s. This very neatly coincides with the known decline in rockhopper numbers.

Just how this reduced food supply translates into a population decline is the subject of further research. Did adults die as a result? Did chicks die or were there not as many chicks produced? And what has prompted the decline in ocean productivity?

This scientific frontier is only just unfolding. The next steps will be to create a profile of subantarctic sea temperatures over time, to relate this profile to ocean food web changes, and to further investigate how food shortages impact on the life history of rockhopper penguins. Because the species is circumpolar, the scientists will collaborate with colleagues in countries such as Argentina, South Africa, France and Britain.

Feeding time for an eastern rockhopper penguin chick at Penguin Bay, Campbell Island.
TUI DE ROY

Human Endeavour

NEW ZEALAND FLAX does not naturally occur at any of the New Zealand subantarctic islands, yet flax bushes are conspicuous on the shores of Port Ross in the Auckland Islands, and their presence poses an intriguing set of questions relating to early human contact with this remote region. A botanist specialising in flax says there are probably two kinds at Port Ross: one typical of the Taranaki region, the other more like flax of Southern New Zealand. How did they get to Port Ross? The Taranaki flax almost certainly was introduced by Ngati Mutunga Maori. Originally from Taranaki, these people arrived at the Port Ross area from the Chatham Islands in 1842, with their Moriori slaves, to establish an extraordinary settlement at the extreme southern margins of Polynesia.

As for the flax from southern New Zealand, no one knows its origin for sure. Did the Maori who accompanied subantarctic sealing expeditions plant some flax bushes? Or were they planted earlier, long before Europeans first ventured into this region?

One of the flax bushes at Erebus Cove, undercut by the lapping tide. NEVILLE PEAT

After years of conjecture about whether pre-European Maori visited – or even settled – some of the New Zealand subantarctic islands, archaeologists now have the evidence that they did. People were burning rata and *Dracophyllum* (grass tree) wood at an occupation site at Sandy Bay, Enderby Island, at least 650 years ago, according to scientific dating of the charcoal remains. Artefacts, fish and bird bones have been recovered from middens at Enderby Island, with the most recent finds being in February 2003. In 1989 a stone knife made of chert, chert flakes and a bone fishhook, possibly made from elephant seal ivory, were all found at Enderby. The source of the chert is unknown. At The Snares in 1961 a 25 cm long stone adze of pre-European design was found at Station Cove, buried in an eroding bank of peat.

Maori artefacts recovered from the subantarctic islands include this adze from The Snares. SOUTHLAND MUSEUM AND ART GALLERY

Sandy Bay, Enderby Island, on a fine summer's day as viewed from a passing Royal New Zealand Air Force Orion aircraft on a subantarctic fisheries patrol. Midden sites are part way along the beach. Sea lions are dotted along the beach and beyond the green sward southern rata flowers redden the forest canopy. Low tundra-like vegetation covers the flat crest of the land.
NEVILLE PEAT

The Snares and Sandy Bay discoveries are building up a picture of exploration of several subantarctic islands by Maori before 1800 – a remarkable feat considering the difficult and unpredictable nature of the intervening seas and rigorous climate.

The first recorded European sightings of the five island groups spanned 22 years, 1788 to 1810 (see page 16), and they opened the floodgates of European commercial exploitation of seals and whales. The sealers came first – secretive ship-based voyages, originating mostly from Sydney and Hobart under British, American and Australian flags. Their policy was to leave no fur seals for a competitor to profit from, and they left virtually no evidence of their calls at the hapless seal colonies. At the start of the 19th century southern seal fur fetched high prices in China and Europe following a decline in Northern Hemisphere fur supplies. New Zealand fur seal skins could be traded for commodities such as spices and silk, and also for slaves. Hats, jackets, muffs and other garments were fashioned from the skins. Elephant seals and sea lions were harvested for oil.

Sealing vessels were active at all five groups. More than 100 trips to the New Zealand subantarctic region are recorded. At the peak of the trade, ships sometimes returned to Sydney with 80,000 to 100,000 skins. By 1827, though, seal populations in southern New Zealand and the subantarctic region had been severely depleted. Sealing became haphazard. The last open season on fur seals in New Zealand was 1946.

It was common for sealing gangs to be left ashore to club and process all the seals in the vicinity. Some gangs became marooned. The record for the longest abandonment probably goes to a gang of four at The Snares. All escaped convicts from Norfolk Island, they were dropped off by the Adventure, whose captain, claiming the vessel was running out of food, told the four they could either stay on board and starve or try their luck ashore. With little more than a few seed potatoes to support them, they opted for the island – and were exiled for eight years. During that time one of the men became so deranged and alarming to his companions, he was pushed over a cliff. In 1817, an American whaling ship rescued the three survivors, who were exonerated of the murder because of their ordeal. Sealing was not for the faint-hearted.

Whaling was the second European industry in southern New Zealand, providing oil for street lamps, spermaceti wax for candles and ambergris for perfume. Petroleum products had yet to be developed; the world relied on natural oils, and whale blubber contained plenty. The baleen whales, humpback and southern right, were hunted both for their oil and for the baleen (whalebone), from which women's corsets, hooped skirts, stays and umbrellas could be manufactured.

Right whales were 'right' for whaling – they were often found close to shore, swam slowly, did not sink after harpooning and yielded large volumes of oil and baleen.

The whaling days at Campbell Island, 1911–14, are recalled by these historic trypots at the site of the Northeast Harbour whaling station. TUI DE ROY

Sealskin footwear made by survivors of the *General Grant* shipwreck. RAKIURA MUSEUM

London prices were high enough at the outset to justify the long voyages to the Southwest Pacific by American and British whalers. The subantarctic region was targeted by deep-sea whaling operations that often involved no port calls in New Zealand. Shore-based whaling, however, was more cost-efficient and from it came some of the earliest European settlements in southern New Zealand.

The ill-fated Enderby settlement at the Auckland Islands grew out of blind optimism regarding the subantarctic region's resource in whales and misleading reports about the suitability of these islands as a site for British colonisation. The first settlers arrived at Port Ross in December 1849, buoyed by the confident predictions of the settlement's leading proponent, Charles Enderby, of the English whaling firm Enderby & Son.

The Enderby people were greeted by the Maori and Moriori settlers, who had been occupying the Port Ross area for seven years after a somewhat desperate exit from the Chatham Islands. The Ngati Mutunga chief Matioro, implicated in the killing of some men from a French whaling vessel at the Chatham Islands and possibly fearing a reprisal, led a group of 40 of his people, with up to 30 Moriori slaves, into a kind of exile at the Auckland Islands. They chartered the brig Hannah for the purpose at a cost of 150 pigs. At Port Ross, when the skipper saw how concerned his passengers were about the climate, soils and food resources of the Auckland Islands, he feared they would demand to go back to the Chathams and promptly weighed anchor, abandoning them.

That they survived until the arrival of the Enderby settlers is testimony to their resourcefulness and ability to withstand hardship. By and large, the two groups got on

The Enderby settlement at Erebus Cove, Port Ross, about 1850, painted by Charles Enderby. ALEXANDER TURNBULL LIBRARY

well. Charles Enderby, Lieutenant-Governor of the prospective colony, appointed Matioro and fellow chief Ngatere as constables, and agreed to pay the Maori inhabitants compensation for their land and pigs.

Within weeks a small town stood at Erebus Cove in Port Ross where once there had been dense rata forest. Enderby had a large house built for himself. Cottages were built for the families, barracks for the single men. The town had a store, workshop and chapel. Enderby envisaged the settlement expanding into a prosperous town development called Hardwicke (the name of the whaling company's principal). But the English were soon disheartened by the poor soils, dismal climate and lack of whales, which had already been decimated by deep-water whaling and the shore stations on mainland New Zealand. Few ships called. Disquiet and dysfunction grew as potatoes and other crops failed. Shoe Island in the middle of Port Ross was declared a prison and unruly members of the community were detained there. The Enderby settlement population peaked at about 300, including the Chatham Islands people and visiting seamen.

By late 1851 the parent company in England, concerned about the lack of revenue, despatched two special commissioners to investigate the affairs of the settlement and close it down if necessary. By August the next year, despite the protestations of the Lieutenant-Governor, the settlement was no more. One of the briefest colonial experiments in British history lasted just two years and nine months. In that time there had been five weddings, 16 births and two infant deaths.

Some Maori and Moriori stayed on. A few departed with the British settlers but others were refused passage in the naval ship that evacuated the British. Two years later, a group of Maori and Moriori were allowed to settle at Port Adventure on Stewart Island/Rakiura and in early 1856, the last of them were uplifted and were returned to the Chatham Islands.

The historic Stella Hut on Enderby Island, built for castaways. NEVILLE PEAT

During this remarkable period of settlement, much use was made of Enderby Island by both groups, and the evidence they left has become mixed up with the scant traces of pre-1800 occupation and later castaway camps. Today, at Erebus Cove, there are only two buildings left: a boatshed and the collapsed remains of a castaway depot, both built after the settlement was abandoned. In the rata and olearia forest behind the cove is evidence of house sites and pathways. A carved inscription, now faint, on the sawn face of a large old rata tree, known as the Victoria Tree, commemorates the visit in 1865 by an Australian government vessel, the *Victoria*, on a routine search for castaways.

A short walk away is a cemetery established by the Enderby settlement. A poignant symbol of the difficulties experienced by the settlers is the headstone of Isabel Younger, who died on 19 November 1850, aged three months. Half the known graves, however, are those of shipwrecked mariners, many of whom arrived a generation later.

At least eight ships were wrecked at the Auckland Islands between 1864 and 1907, with the loss of 121 lives.

Left: The historic cemetery at Erebus Cove, Port Ross. NEVILLE PEAT

Right: Baby Isabel Younger's headstone in the historic cemetery at Erebus Cove. She died at the age of three months in 1850. GEOFF WALLS

Why so many wrecks at so remote a place? The group's location astride the wind-assisted Great Circle trading route is the underlying reason. Ships travelling westwards from Australia to Europe via Cape Horn ducked under mainland New Zealand. But first they had to clear the New Zealand subantarctic islands and the Auckland group in particular, which lay right in the path of many sailing ships. Misplacement of the islands on some charts confused navigators but cloudy weather, preventing the use of a sextant to find coordinates, probably put more ships at peril.

Apart from the sealing vessel *Perseverance*, which was wrecked at Campbell Island in 1829, and the three ships that were lost at the Antipodes Islands, all other recorded shipwrecks in the New Zealand subantarctic region occurred at the Auckland Islands.

Ironically, the first wreck could not be blamed on suspect navigation. A small schooner from Sydney, the *Grafton*, was washed ashore in Carnley Harbour in a violent storm in January 1864. Her captain, Thomas Musgrave, French prospector Francois-Edouard Raynal (who had been looking for tin deposits), and three crew members lived in a hut built of salvaged materials for 19 months before Musgrave, Raynal and one of the crew set out for Stewart Island/Rakiura in the refitted ship's dinghy. They arrived safely five days later and from there Musgrave organised the rescue of the two remaining castaways.

As the *Grafton* survivors eked out an existence at the south end of the group that year, the three-masted clipper ship *Invercauld*, bound for Chile, was wrecked near the northwest corner of the main island. Nineteen of the ship's company of 25 struggled ashore. All but three succumbed in the cold, wet winter months ahead. Several died of exposure, others of starvation. Four died crossing the high hills to Port Ross, just 10 km from the wreck site. The *Grafton* survivors knew nothing of the tragedy unfolding to the north of them.

The most famous wreck of all occurred in May 1866 when the big three-masted barque *General Grant* met her end under the forbidding western cliffs of Auckland Island, carrying wool, hides, timber and gold. Of the 83 passengers and crew, 68 perished, and five of the 15 survivors died subsequently. By the time they were rescued by the sealing vessel *Amherst*, the 10 survivors, including one woman, had been marooned for 18 months. Several expeditions searched unsuccessfully for the remains of the *General Grant*, and her gold bullion in particular, through the 20th century.

Following the loss of the *General Grant* the New Zealand Government stepped up provisioning for castaways at the Auckland Islands. Wooden depots were erected – the first in 1880 at Enderby Island, just above Sandy Bay – and these depots were equipped with tools, matches, fishing gear, clothing, blankets, medicine and food in the form of tinned meat and biscuits. Government ships serviced the depots until 1923.

When the iron barque *Derry Castle* was dashed to pieces on the northern point of Enderby Island in March 1887, the Sandy Bay castaway depot should have been a godsend for the 8 survivors. Instead, as a result of looting, it contained only a bottle of salt. Bound for England with a cargo of Australian wheat, the *Derry Castle* struck the reef that now bears her name. Had she been sailing 100 metres to the north on that wet and squally night, she would have been in clear water. In a makeshift punt, the survivors managed to get to the well-stocked castaway depot at Erebus Cove and after four months they were rescued.

The punt from the *Derry Castle*, which served for a time as the headstone for the mass grave on Enderby Island, is now in the Southland Museum, and the ship's figurehead is housed in Canterbury Museum.

The mass grave of victims of the *Derry Castle* shipwreck on Enderby Island, as it appeared in the late 1880s. The vessel's figurehead, (now in the Canterbury Museum), stands at the head of the grave. SOUTHLAND MUSEUM AND ART GALLERY

Another notable wreck was that of the four-masted barque *Dundonald*, which was driven on to the rocky shores of Disappointment Island in March 1907, with her holds filled with Australian wheat. Twelve crew died from drowning in the surf or battering on the rocks. The 16 survivors built huts out of *Hebe* branches with tussock thatch, and they survived by eating mollymawks, seals and the Macquarie Island cabbage *Stilbocarpa polaris*.

Desperate to escape the bleak and exposed island, where food and firewood were limited, they built a flimsy coracle out of branches and seal skins in order to reach the main island and the depot at Erebus Cove. Twelve weeks after their ship sank the survivors were rescued by the New Zealand Government steamer *Hinemoa*, one of the ships that serviced the castaway depots. A coracle similar to the one used to escape from Disappointment Island was collected from the island by the rescuers and is housed at Canterbury Museum.

There have been few shipwrecks in the modern era but in June 1999 the 11-metre Auckland-built yacht *Totorore* was lost at Antipodes Island. She had been due to pick up a party of albatross researchers. Wreckage was discovered in South Bay but no trace of owner-skipper Gerry Clark or his crewman Roger Sales was found.

First-hand Accounts

THERE ARE SEVERAL FIRST-HAND ACCOUNTS of being shipwrecked at the Auckland Islands – and each graphically describes the initial shock and agony followed by the chronic hardship and deprivation as they awaited rescue.

Charles Eyres, a survivor of the *Dundonald* wreck of 1907, recalled the first dawn:

> a group of shivering, bleeding castaways standing on the edge of those black cliffs in the grey light of the morning, whilst below us the waves dashed, and the masts of our poor ship stuck up like gravestones marking where she lay ... I cannot describe the cold ... we trembled with it so that we could not keep still ... Most of us, too, had very little clothing and the majority of us had kicked off our boots ...

Robert Holding, a survivor from the *Invercauld* wreck of 1864, wrote a detailed account of the ordeal that included securing pig meat on the ninth day after the wreck:

> ... under a large rock we saw the pig. We lost no time in trying to release it, but it being jammed too tight we had to get a plank as a leaver [sic], and while the rest tried to prise up the rock, I took it by the hind legs. Guess my surprise when it came in two across the loins. I figured it at about 120 lbs. but ROTTEN I should think. The reader will perhaps say, "I would not of eaten that", but circumstances alter the cases. Please consider our position, then I think you will see that we had to eat anything we could obtain or die where we were. I don't wish to dwell upon that subject, it is too abhorrent.

Survivors of the wreck of the *Dundonald* in 1907 built these huts of *Hebe* branches and tussock grasses on Disappointment Island. ALEXANDER TURNBULL LIBRARY

Government steamers on their half-yearly visits during the late 1870s and 1880s would regularly release animals at all groups but the Bounty Islands for use by castaways. Goats, for example, were dropped off at Campbell Island, Auckland Island, Antipodes Island and The Snares but either died out or were culled. Cattle and sheep did not survive at Antipodes Island. Steamer crews cut firewood for fuel at the various islands, and these areas can still be identified.

Farming was attempted at the larger subantarctic islands despite the bleak experience of the Enderby settlers, the warnings from Captain Musgrave (*Grafton*) and others about the acid soils, and the obvious remoteness. The first serious attempt came in 1874 when Dr F.A. Monkton, of Invercargill, sent a couple, Mr and Mrs Nelson, to Port Ross to establish a sheep and cattle farm on a Government pastoral lease. The Nelsons built a house at Erebus Cove but were poorly serviced and returned to the mainland within three years. Pastoral farming attempts continued on Auckland Island and also on Adams Island but without long-term success. In 1900, 2000 sheep were reportedly landed at Circular Head in Carnley Harbour but they died out in a few years, the last being sighted in 1907.

Campbell Island, despite its more southerly location, proved to be more hospitable to farming. In 1895, a Gisborne man, J. Gordon, took up a Government lease at Campbell Island. He built a homestead and woolshed at Tucker Cove near the head of Perseverance Harbour and released 300 to 400 sheep. In 1900, he sold out to Captain W.H. Tucker, also of Gisborne, who later engaged shore whalers from the New Zealand mainland to tend the sheep and undertake whaling from Northwest Bay and Northeast Harbour in the winter. Tucker sold the lease, stock and buildings to a Dunedin syndicate in 1916.

About this time Campbell Island sheep farming peaked, with outputs in one year including 6,800 sheep shorn, 1,600 lambs and a wool clip of 131 bales. The isolation was a telling factor, however, with a tenuous supply line and few comforts amid a trying climate. In 1931, farming was abandoned.

The Second World War introduced the next era of human occupation: coastwatching. It was sparked by the 'Erlangen incident'. In 1939, with war imminent, the German merchant ship *Erlangen* departed in a hurry from Otago Harbour and headed for the Auckland Islands to load wood to fuel her boilers. Her crew laboured to

Crew members of the New Zealand Government steamship *Hinemoa* with the frame of a boat used by survivors of the *Dundonald* shipwreck to escape from Disappointment Island.
ALEXANDER TURNBULL LIBRARY

Radio operator C. Young at work during the coastwatch expedition to the Auckland Islands during World War II.
ALEXANDER TURNBULL LIBRARY

cut 235 tons of rata over several weeks. When the New Zealand Government heard of the incident, it decided to mount a coast watch at Auckland and Campbell Islands. Code-named the Cape Expedition, the coastwatchers established stations at Ranui Cove in Port Ross, Tagua Bay in Carnley Harbour and Tucker Cove in Perseverance Harbour. Three vessels took it in turn to service the stations – the auxiliary schooner *Tagua* and the auxiliary ketches *Ranui* and *New Golden Hind*.

Cape Expedition members included a number of leading scientists, among them geologist/paleontologist Charles Fleming and naturalist Robert Falla, both of whom were later knighted for their services to science. Ornithologist Graham Turbott and naturalist Jack Sorensen also served as coastwatchers. In addition to keeping an eye out for enemy shipping the Cape Expedition advanced knowledge of the geology, landforms, flora, fauna and climate of the two subantarctic groups.

Auckland Islands maps became more accurate thanks to the Cape Expedition's survey expertise. A survey team led by Allan Eden produced the first comprehensive triangulation network – the basis of the modern topographical map of the group. Allan Eden believed

Timber piles from the old wharf at Ranui Cove, the site of a World War II coastwatch station near Port Ross.
CHRIS CARROLL

that, although the Admiralty charts used by 19th century windjammers had 'many large errors, none is sufficiently serious to be blamed for any of the wrecks, with the possible exception of the *Derry Castle*.'

The Tucker Cove base on Campbell Island was kept open as a weather station after the war ended. In 1957 a new meteorological station was built at Beeman Point in time for the International Geophysical Year of 1957–58, a milestone in international scientific research and cooperation. The Campbell Island station contributed to the network of atmospheric observations. Tides, earthquakes and geomagnetic changes were also measured. From then through to its conversion to an automatic operation in 1995, the Campbell Island station typically had a staff of 12, appointed for 12 months at a time. Although the buildings remain, the station is no longer permanently staffed but part of the complex is utilised periodically by scientists and Department of Conservation management staff.

The Conservation Management Strategy says that, in keeping with the nature reserve status of the islands, facilities and structures built on the islands since the end of World War II should be removed. But the strategy also flags the historic significance of the met station, and in years to come it could provide a valuable insight into the way weather and climate trends were observed and recorded in the latter half of the 20th century.

Cost, isolation and transport are limiting factors when it comes to heritage conservation at the islands. Some ten percent of these historic sites are identified as priority sites in the Conservation Management Strategy. They include the Stella castaway hut on Enderby Island, Erebus Cove cemetery and German scientific site at Terror Cove. Conservation work has been undertaken on all surviving fingerposts and a number of castaway buildings and World War II lookout huts.

In the latter half of the 20th century, with advances in technology, transport and communications, the New Zealand subantarctic region's marine resources grew in importance. Licences were issued to fishing companies operating in the region's vast Exclusive Economic Zone. Fishing in these southern waters is now a major industry. In the 1970s and 1980s there was interest among petroleum companies in prospecting for undersea hydrocarbon deposits in the Great South Basin of the Campbell Plateau. A few exploratory holes were drilled, including in 1983 a hole 240 km east of The Snares. To date there has been no mining for oil or minerals.

As for the islands themselves, nature and historic heritage protection is the ruling land use today, and tourism the only permitted commercial enterprise. Two hundred years ago people came for the sealing; today they visit mainly to study or experience the extraordinary nature of the islands and their equally fascinating human history.

Trade in penguin skins

IN 1880–81, a Bluff merchant, Walter Henderson, started a trade in penguin skins, most of which were turned into hand-warming muffs for ladies, fashionable at the time. Crested penguins were obtained mainly from the colonies at the Antipodes and Snares Islands. Some seal skins and seal oil were also harvested. By the time the trade stopped, having become unprofitable, Henderson had purchased more than 15,000 skins.

A relic of the 19th-century penguin trade: a bundle of penguin skins cached under a rock overhang on Antipodes Island. KATH WALKER

1840 and all that

IN THE YEAR 1840, when New Zealand became a nation, exploration of the New Zealand subantarctic region took a huge leap forward. No fewer than three international expeditions called at the Auckland Islands that year.

Two separate expeditions – the United States Exploring Expedition under the command of Charles Wilkes and a French expedition under Dumont D'Urville – arrived at the Auckland Islands from Antarctic waters in March, coincidentally on the same day. Wilkes pronounced Port Ross, then known as the Bay of Sarah's Bosom, an excellent place to refit a ship and take on water and wood, and he noted the presence of whalers, who had planted vegetables. The French, in the *Astrolabe*, stayed eight days compared to the Americans' four days and their reports reveal a greater interest in the geography, flora and fauna of the group.

But the most valuable studies were made by the British Antarctic Expedition, with two ships, *Erebus* and *Terror*, under the command of Sir James Clark Ross. Heading for the Ross Sea area of Antarctica towards the end of the year, the expedition visited the Auckland Islands for three weeks and Campbell Island for five days. Whereas the scientists made an intensive study of the nature of the islands (see page 69), Ross was impressed by the harbour at the north end of the Auckland group, which he considered had the makings of a successful penal settlement if not a settlement based on whaling.

Members of the 1874 German scientific expedition beside apparatus they mounted at Terror Cove to observe the Transit of Venus. The remains of the plinth behind them can still be seen at the cove.
LA TROBE PICTURE COLLECTION, STATE LIBRARY OF VICTORIA

Dumont D'Urville's French exploring expedition of 1840 involved the ships *Astrolabe* and *Zélée*, portrayed here at Shoe Island in Port Ross by the expedition artist Louis le Breton.
ALEXANDER TURNBULL LIBRARY

Transit of Venus

EVERY CENTURY OR SO, the planet Venus passes across the face of the sun. These transits occur in pairs, eight years apart, and in earlier times they shed light on the size of the solar system. In particular, they allowed astronomers to calculate the distance between the sun and Earth. James Cook's first visit to Tahiti in 1769 was to observe the Transit of Venus, and in 1874 another opportunity arose. The next transits are in 2004 and 2012. Only the 2012 transit will be visible from New Zealand.

Of the five European expeditions despatched to the Southern Ocean to observe the 1874 Transit of Venus, two came to the New Zealand subantarctic region: the French to Campbell Island and a German party to the Auckland Islands.

The many French names at Campbell Island are a legacy of that visit. For example, Jacquemart Island is named after the captain of the expedition ship *Vire* (Vire Point), Courrejolles Peninsula is named after the expedition photographer, and tooth-shaped Dent Island is descriptive. The names of various peaks are patently French or connected to the work of the expedition: Paris, Azimuth, Fizeau are examples. Dr Henry Filhol was the expedition surgeon and naturalist, whose name is attached to a peak and also to the eastern rockhopper penguin.

Based at Venus Bay next to Garden Cove, the innermost part of Perseverance Harbour, the French stayed three and a half months. Sadly, cloudy weather spoiled their observations of the transit but at the Auckland Islands the Germans struck it lucky. Of the 9 December event, they reported: '… at 12 o'clock a gentle wind sprang up, which cleared the fog and broke the clouds in front of the sun just before the phenomenon occurred.' A quarter of an hour after the transit, cloud again covered the sun.

They had set up their house and observatories at Terror Cove in Port Ross after arriving in the French barque *Alexandrine* from Melbourne on 15 October. During the transit their astronomers obtained six complete sets of angles. A total of 115 photographs were taken. The Germans also studied geomagnetic features during their stay but had little opportunity to explore beyond Port Ross.

Only the main instrument pillars remain at Terror Cove together with a plaque commemorating the expedition.

The German Transit of Venus Expedition of 1874 constructed these buildings at Terror Cove in the Auckland Islands.

LA TROBE PICTURE COLLECTION, STATE LIBRARY OF VICTORIA

Boardwalk construction across Enderby Island's tundra-like herbfield. The walkway will reduce the trampling impact of visitors.
DEPARTMENT OF CONSERVATION

6 The Pull of the Deep South

At Campbell Island, a boardwalk defines the popular track to the saddle between Col Peak and Mt Lyall.
WYNSTON COOPER

Left: Visitors to the Bounty Islands cruise close inshore in one of their vessel's small boats.
DAVID AGNEW

A RARE AND VULNERABLE kind of heritage, the New Zealand subantarctic islands – all five groups – have attracted a passing parade of people since William Bligh mapped the Bounty Islands in 1788 and wrote about their curious 'white spots'. People have come for commercial and scientific reasons. In relatively recent times, they have come simply to experience awesome wildlife in a remote and physically challenging setting.

The first tourists to visit the islands in modern times arrived aboard the *Magga Dan* in 1968 en route to the Ross Sea area of Antarctica, which was the main drawcard. But as the entrancing nature of the islands became apparent, and films, television documentaries and magazine articles played up the fascination, tour ships began offering the subantarctic as a destination in itself.

In December 1988, the first New Zealand-based tours were initiated by the 20-passenger sailing vessel *Tradewind*, operating out of Bluff and Dunedin. Today other vessels make up to ten visits a season to the region, and sometimes a tour going to the Auckland and Campbell groups will also take in Macquarie Island. Subantarctic tourism, offering an ecotourism experience, is substantially the domain of chartered small to medium-sized tour ships, including a number of versatile Russian research vessels. A few private motor yachts also bring visitors.

Plenty of people want to visit these islands. There are risks and potential impacts from all visits, whether they are for management purposes, scientific research, information or tourism. Strict rules apply to all types of visitor. A precautionary approach is essential. The multiple risks faced by the indigenous fauna and flora, the history of incursions and adverse impacts, and the unique nature of the islands compared to anywhere else on earth – these are all factors that justify a directive to tread carefully.

Where tourism is concerned, rules on where visitors can and cannot go, and how many should be allowed at any one site, are based on the Conservation Management Strategy's assessment of vulnerability and other factors. The sites where tourists are allowed to land are classified 'large' or 'small' depending on the numbers they can handle. There are only three 'large' sites – Enderby Island and the historic Enderby settlement/cemetery site in the Auckland Islands, and the Beeman Point/Col-Lyall Saddle boardwalk site on Campbell Island. Three to four hours are required for the return trip on the Campbell Island boardwalk, and a similar amount of time is needed to explore Enderby Island. A limit of 600 visitors per season applies to these sites, and no more than 150 visitors a day can land.

Young New Zealand (Hooker's) sea lions socialising at Derry Castle Reef, Enderby Island. ANDRIS APSE

A few other places – the more vulnerable 'small' sites – have been identified at Auckland and Campbell Islands. These sites receive no more than 150 visitors a season. They include Northwest Bay on Campbell Island and two historic coastwatch stations at Auckland Island.

A Minimum Impact Code issued to the visitors before they land sets out the dos and don'ts. Visitors are asked to keep to formed tracks and boardwalks in order to limit damage to fragile soils and plants. All wildlife has the right of way and must not be disturbed. A 5-metre safety margin applies when viewing sea lions, fur seals, elephant seals, penguins, albatrosses and other birds. The code reminds visitors that disturbance to nesting birds can lead to the loss of eggs through exposure or predation. Brown skua are awake to any opportunity.

Guides must accompany passengers at a ratio of 1 to 20, and no walking at will is permitted. Each ship carries a Department of Conservation representative to provide advice and oversee activities.

Mt Lyall, 400 m above sea level, is a giant arrowhead on the ridge between Perseverance Harbour (right) and Northeast Harbour.
TUI DE ROY

Impact fee

IN THE NEW ZEALAND subantarctic region, visitors help pay for managing tourism and for the maintenance of facilities such as tracks and boardwalks. A Tourism Impact Management Fee is levied on each visitor. The fee also offsets the cost of a visitor monitoring programme, quarantine contingencies such as rodent bait stations at strategic places, and the assignment of a Department of Conservation representative on each trip.

Heavy traffic: this granite slope at The Snares is a popular landing and departure point for the endemic penguins of these islands. CHRIS CARROLL

World Heritage Area listing, which is likely to boost visitor numbers or at least sustain the interest, has reinforced the need to minimise damage or adverse impacts. Not all the impacts occur on land. In June 2002, the Department of Conservation placed a 10-year moratorium on the issuing of permits for commercial whale viewing at the Auckland Islands between April and October, the breeding season for southern right whales at Port Ross. The department made this decision out of concern the nature tourism industry might target the Auckland Islands for winter whale tours and disturb the whales' breeding.

Tourist landings are not permitted at the Bounty, Snares and Antipodes Islands because of their highly vulnerable nature and the application of the precautionary principle. Tour ships, nonetheless, sometimes give passengers a look at these islands from the sea, using inflatable dinghies to get in close.

The Snares group is more often approached than the Bounty or Antipodes groups because it lies close to the route between mainland New Zealand and the Auckland Islands. At The Snares, inshore cruising can be just as rewarding and spectacular as a landing. From a dinghy there are better views of the cliffs and penguins' landing spots than from the land, and there are often sea lions and fur seals playing in the water. Land birds such as the endemic Snares fernbird and tomtit are sometimes sighted.

Many visitors to the New Zealand subantarctic region find the relics of human endeavour as fascinating as the landforms and the flora and fauna. At the Auckland and Campbell groups, visitors need to be carefully controlled in and around old buildings and other structures, shipwreck sites and so on. In the past, unknown and unpermitted parties have damaged some sites or souvenired artefacts. If anything, these historic resources are more fragile than the island's indigenous life and in many cases only ruins remain.

Besides the poignancy there is a powerful message. These fading human imprints have become a graphic metaphor for the transience of people in a region now wholly turned over to nature.

Roaring Forties Experience

FEW PEOPLE will get to experience the New Zealand subantarctic islands first hand. But at the Southland Museum and Art Gallery in Invercargill is a 'next best thing' – a gallery that conveys the sights, sounds and sensations of the New Zealand sub-antarctic islands. Unique in New Zealand, this subantarctic gallery, developed in conjunction with the Department of Conservation, encap-sulates the human and natural history of the region. Special exhibits include a gruff-voiced sea lion in its rata forest lair and a simulated 19th century shipwreck experience – the moving forepeak of the *General Grant*, trapped by westerly winds and waves in a sea cave at the Auckland Islands. The gallery has proved also to be of great interest to those who have visited the islands.

Close by, in the Queens Park Gardens, check on progress with establishing a garden featuring megaherbs from the New Zealand subantarctic islands.

INDEX

Bold numbers = main reference

Italicised numbers = illustrations

A westerly gale churns the waters of Port Ross. ANDRIS APSE

Further Reading

Allen, Madelene Ferguson, 1997. *Wake of the Invercauld – shipwrecked in the sub-Antarctic: a great granddaughter's pilgrimage*, Exisle Publishing, Auckland.

Atkinson, Tudor, 2001. *St Michael Goes South: A 31 foot motor-sailor in support of the 1972/73 Auckland Islands Scientific Expedition*, Department of Conservation Wellington.

Bailey, Alfred M. and Sorensen, J.H., 1962. *Subantarctic Campbell Island*, Denver Museum of Natural History.

Clark, M.R. and P.R. Dingwall, 1985, reprinted 1990. *Conservation of Islands in the Southern Ocean*, IUCN/ Cambridge University Press, England.

Department of Conservation, 1998. *Conservation Management Strategy: Subantarctic Islands 1998–2008*, Southland Conservancy Conservation Management Planning Series No. 10.

Dingwall, P.R. C. Fraser, J.G. Gregory, C.J.R. Robertson (eds), 1999. *Enderby Settlement Diaries: Records of a British Colony at the Auckland Islands 1849–1852*, Wild Press, Wellington/Wordsell Press, Pakuranga.

Dingwall, P.R., J.G. Gregory (eds), 2004. *A Musterer's sojourn on Campbell Island: the diary of Alfred Austin 1919–1921*, Department of Conservation, Wellington.

Dingwall, Paul R.; Jones, Kevin L.; Egerton, Rachael (eds), in press 2006. *In care of the Southern Ocean: an archaeological and historical survey of the Auckland Islands*. Department of Conservation, Wellington.

Eden, A.W., 1955. *Islands of Despair*, Melrose, London.

Escott-Inman, H., 1911. *The Castaways of Disappointment Island*, Patridge, London.

Eunson, Keith, 1971. *The Wreck of the General Grant*, Reed, Wellington.

Fraser, Conon, 1986. *Beyond the Roaring Forties*, Government Printing Office, Wellington.

Heather, Barrie and Hugh Robertson, 1996. *The Field Guide to the Birds of New Zealand*, Viking/Penguin Books, Auckland.

Kerr, I.S., 1976. *Campbell Island: A History*, Reed, Wellington.

McEwen, Mary (ed.), in press 2006. *Charles Fleming's Cape Expedition Diary, Auckland Islands 1942–1943.*

Detail from page 42. KIM WESTERSKOV

McNab, R., 1907. *Murihiku and the Southern Islands*, William Smith, Invercargill.

McNab, R., 1909. *Murihiku*, Whitcombe & Tombs, Wellington.

Musgrave, T., 1943. *Castaway on the Auckland Islands*, Reed, Wellington.

Onley, Derek and Sandy Bartle, 1999, reprinted 2001. *Identification of the Seabirds of the Southern Ocean: a guide for scientific observers aboard fishing vessels*, Te Papa Press/CCAMLR.

Peat, Neville, Les Molloy and Paul Dingwall, *Nomination of the New Zealand Subantarctic Islands by the Government of New Zealand for inclusion in the World Heritage List*, Department of Conservation, 1997.

Poppleton, George, 2000. *Campbell Island 1955–56, 1958–60*, Jenn Falconer, Wellington.

Taylor, Rowley, 2006. *Straight Through from London (Antipodes and Bounty Islands history and natural history)*, Heritage Expeditions.

Turbott, Graham, 2002. *Year Away: Wartime Coastwatching on the Auckland Islands, 1944.* Department of Conservation, Wellington.

Viney, Chris, 2001. *Macquarie Island*, Tasmanian Parks & Wildlife Service/Tasmanian Department of Primary Industries, Water and Environment, Hobart.